FEGEN AND NORRISS'

GORDON BRITTAS

SHARING THE DREAM

FEGEN AND NORRISS'

GORDON BRITTAS

SHARING THE DREAM

BY JONATHAN RICE

B🌿XTREE

First published in Great Britain in 1994 by
Boxtree Limited, Broadwall House, 21 Broadwall, London SE1 9PL

Brittas format and television scripts copyright ©
Richard Fegan and Andrew Norriss, 1994

Text copyright © Jonathan Rice, 1994

Designed by Design 23, London

Photographs of Gordon Brittas by Paul Forrester
Additional photographs by courtesy of the BBC and Hulton Deutsch

Printed and bound in the UK by
Cambus Litho, East Kilbride, Glasgow

A CIP catalogue entry for this book is available from the British Library

10 9 8 7 6 5 4 3 2 1

ISBN: 0 7522 0896 9

ACKNOWLEDGEMENTS

In preparing this work, I have been greatly helped by many other people, although of course the basic philosophy is my own. I particularly appreciate the efforts put in by my parents, my family and my loyal staff, without whom the Whitbury New Town Leisure Centre would not be in the condition it is today. Richard Fegen, Andrew Norriss and Chris Barrie have between them helped me bring my thoughts to a wider public, by putting into words and actions some of the deeper recesses of my mind. I am also grateful to my editor, who, despite clearly not understanding much of what is written here, nevertheless has not ever doubted what my words are truly worth.

I am less grateful to the Whitbury Printing and Publicity Co. Ltd., who were given the task of preparing and printing many of the publicity materials used in our many campaigns to bring my Dream to an unsuspecting public. Their badges reading "I've been to Whitbury Leisure Centre and swum in the poo" had to be returned. Their explanation that the final letter on the word 'pool' had just slipped round the edge a bit was not acceptable. They also managed to print one hundred thousand publicity leaflets for this book (to allow for each inhabitant of Whitbury as well as several extra for visitors to the Leisure Centre from out of town) with the legend "Gordon Brittas – Sharing The Cream", which they then corrected to "Shaving the Dream".

I hope you enjoy this book. All facts have been checked and cross-checked. All errors are my responsibility alone. Or the Whitbury Printing and Publicity Co. Ltd's. More likely theirs, in fact.

The Hon.
Seb Coe, MP

ALDERSHOT

Aldershot was where it all began for me. I don't mean that that was where I was born. I was born in Romford. Nor, for that matter, is Aldershot where we lived or where I went to school. Come to that, I didn't go to university in Aldershot, either, largely because there is no university in Aldershot, unless the Aldershot Military School of Needlework, Knitting and Crochet has been turned into the North Hampshire University or some such in the latest educational reshuffles. I am a graduate of Loughborough, *alma mater* of the Hon. Sebastian Coe MP among many others.

But Aldershot is where it all began for me in the Leisure industry. After Romford, after Mrs. Wilson's kindergarten, the Abattoir Road Primary School and the Sir Anthony Blunt Grammar School for Boys, after Loughborough College and my B.A. in Sports Administration, my mission in life began in Aldershot. My Dream was first put into action there. My first faltering steps on the road to world peace and harmony through sports and leisure were taken in that picturesque little town 34 miles south west of London on the Hampshire/Surrey border. Aldershot was where I first worked at a Leisure Centre.

It was an invigorating experience. We tried to put into effect all the ideas

A

that I had developed over years of preparation and study, although not all of them could immediately be put to the test. For example, Aldershot, being a military town, is not perhaps the very best place to start a campaign to end all wars, as it would involve many members of the population of that town being thrown out of work, which in turn would hardly help another part of my Dream to come true - the Abolition of Poverty. It's no good having the rest of the world living in peace and financial security if Aldershot is left in abject poverty and depression. My Dream is for all people, not just those who do not live in Aldershot.

I think we could have made greater strides than we did, if it had not been for the unfortunate way my work there ended. Under circumstances which I have never fully been able to understand, the Leisure Centre at Aldershot collapsed during one of my days in temporary charge (I was only a Deputy Manager at this time: greater things were to await me at Whitbury). Official estimates later put the damage at £3.5 million, which was unfortunate for the local taxpayers, but luckily very few people were seriously injured. And somebody had to dig them out. We had a good team at Aldershot.

Anyway, after Aldershot I was promoted to become manager of my own Leisure Centre at Whitbury New Town, one of the most beautiful new conurbations in the South of England. At last, the lessons of Aldershot could be put into practice, and the Dream could be shared with the world.

BACK-UP TEAM (THE)

It has taken me some time, but I now believe that I have the makings of a first class staff supporting me in my role as Manager of Whitbury New Town Leisure Centre. Not all of them are yet fully committed to my Dream, in the way that any good leisure executive ought to be if he (or she) wishes to reach the very top, but in many ways it is a distinct advantage to the smooth running of my Leisure centre that the rest of my team are not cut out for higher things. It means that everybody knows his (or her) place, and leaves to me the important decisions that only a natural leader and trained manager like myself can cope with. All the same, they are a fine team, forged and bonded over the months, welded into a unit. You could not, as I told Bri Kitson, the Southern Areas Inspector, ask for a better crowd. They are dedicated, loyal, keen, professional and competent. They reflect the strengths of their captain, and we set the standards by which other Leisure Centres ought to be judged.

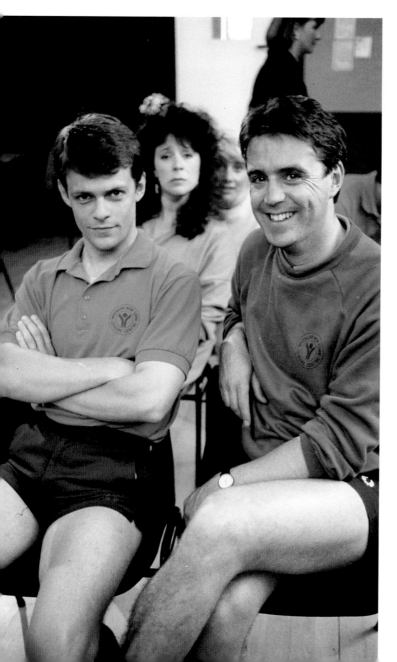

Featherly, Gavin (I start with Gavin simply because I like to take my team in alphabetical order) is a good bloke. He runs the SlimTrim classes, and seems to understand the chubby young wives who attend just perfectly, and they him. 'Caring, sharing Gavin' I call him, for he is the one whose

Gavin with Tim

concern for others is perfectly expressed in the way he washes out Carole's children's nappies and cooks meals for his friend Tim. I believe he may have management qualities hidden beneath that clean green sports shirt and those trim blue shorts.

Lancing, Laura – or to be more strictly correct Laura Farrell, as she once made the enormous error of marrying that remarkably unattractive example of the American race, Michael T. Farrell III - is my Deputy Manager (Dry). There is no doubt that she is a useful deputy. As I wrote in the reference I gave her when she was applying for a job to be manager in a Leisure Centre in Teddington, "she would be a good choice, for a woman", and I can hardly give higher praise than that. All the same, she didn't get the job.

I used to wonder whether she was in love with me. She once grabbed me by the ears, pulled me to her and gave me a long and reasonably passionate kiss, for no apparent reason. I must confess to being surprised as I had always thought of Laura as being devoid of deep emotions. And not with such strong biceps. But I asked Helen about it and she put me right.

"Helen, have you ever thought that Laura might perhaps be in love with me?"

"Laura?"

"Yes. I mean it wouldn't be the first time. The older, more experienced man, the young, reasonably attractive assistant who..."

"No, Gordon."

"Are you sure?" It was a fairly long kiss, after all.

"Gordon, my mind's gone on a lot of things but, I promise you, Laura is not in love with you. In fact, she's often told me how very annoying she finds you."

That is exactly what she was telling me immediately before she broke off in mid-sentence to kiss me. I don't think I will ever understand women.

Parkinson, Carole (our receptionist) is one woman I am certain that I will never understand. She has at long last mastered the art of greeting all visitors to the centre with a bright smile and the words, "Good morning. Welcome to Whitbury Leisure Centre. How may I help you?", but I have a feeling that her whole life does not revolve around her work. This is perhaps surprising in that her whole family certainly revolves around Whitbury Leisure Centre. Indeed, her whole family seems to live in some of the deepest recesses of Whitbury Leisure Centre.

Carole has three children, Ben, and the twins Emily and Tom, who were born in the Leisure Centre's sauna room, and they seem to be spending their childhood in the drawers of the reception area. This is not something of which I approve, but seeing that young Carole has managed to acquire her children without bothering with the legalities of a relationship first, I have come to the conclusion that it is best to let Carole get on with her life in her own way, although I do still try to give advice from time to time. In fact, she conceived the twins without even knowing who the father was, which seems to me to be a peculiarly slapdash way of breeding. It is not the sort of thing that I would ever want to be a party to. But Carole lacks self-confidence, which might explain why she never bucked up the courage to introduce herself to this man to whom she nevertheless opened the Temple of her Body. I try very hard to build up her self-image, to make her look more positively at herself, but she has so many other problems in her life that, as I have told her more than once, perhaps it is just too great a task for someone as plain and ordinary as her.

It is good advice, that, and although I gave it on that occasion to Carole, it could equally well apply to everyone. Let's get on with our own jobs. I'll run Whitbury Leisure Centre, Carole will try as best she can to keep the reception.

WHITBURY NEW TOWN LEISURE CENTRE
NEW STAFF INTAKE JOB APPLICATION FORM

(to be completed in triplicate: The WHITE COPY is to be handed into Personnel; the GREEN COPY is to retained by the candidate; the PINK COPY is to be posted on the Job Application notice board for a period of not less than three weeks, in case anybody knows of any just impediment why they should not be employed).

SECTION 1: PERSONAL DETAILS
NAME................................
DATE OF BIRTH..
PLACE OF BIRTH..
NAME OF HOSPITAL..
NAME AND CURRENT ADDRESS OF MIDWIFE or
MATERNITY WARD SISTER (to verify the facts of your birth)
....

SECTION 2: FAMILY DETAILS
NAME OF FATHER (if known)................................
OCCUPATION OF FATHER (if kown)................................
NAME OF MOTHER................................
CURRENT ADDRESS OF FATHER AND/OR MOTHER (if Known)
....
NAMES AND DATES OF BIRTH OF BROTHERS AND SISTERS (if any)
....
....

SECTION 3: EDUCATION DETAILS
NAME AND ADDRESS OF PLAYGROUP................................
NAME AND ADDRESS OF LEADER OF PLAYGOUP................................
DATES OF ATTENDANCE AT PLAYGROUP................................
DETAILS OF PROJECTS WORKED ON AT PLAYGOUP (eg Building Lego bricks, Potato Cut painting, making devices out of toilet rolls and sticky back plastic; please show examples of work where possible..........................
NAME AND ADDRESS OF PRIMARY SCHOOL................................
....
NAME AND ADDRESS AND PROFESSIONAL

Perkin, Linda is one of the keenest, liveliest members of our staff. She adds a bright smile to all that goes on in our happy Centre, and might have had, I thought, the makings of a true Leisure professional. But she is another example of a woman who is hard to understand.

I once gave my staff a questionnaire to fill out, to help me understand their hopes and ambitions for the future. You know, the usual sort of questions: "Would you like to take part in working towards an ideal which will one day play a major part in promoting world harmony and peace?" (to which Tim - see below - replied with just one word: 'No'); and "Would you be prepared to give a whole-hearted and full time commitment to helping others find their place in the community through the medium of sport?" (which Gavin - see above - thought worthy of a 'Not really.'). Just ordinary straightforward questions that any good manager would routinely ask his staff.

Linda was the only one who filled it in properly, but when I suggested that she was the person who could help me carry the torch of Harmony Through Sport into the next century, she locked herself in the stationery cupboard. All I said was, "Linda, I have something very precious to pass on to you," and she leapt into the cupboard and bolted the door. Eventually Laura managed to explain that my words were metaphorical rather than literal, and she came back out into the light.

Porter, Julie is my secretary. She comes from somewhere in the north of England, which makes both her accent and her actions difficult to comprehend at times. She is an individual in her own right, and I respect that, of course, but there are times when I wonder whether she brings the right attitude with her to the workplace. One day I hope she may make a cup of coffee for one of my visitors, rather than just shrugging her shoulders and saying she'd rather not bother, but I respect her right to fill the working hours in the way she feels most constructive for the Leisure Centre. One day, perhaps, her views on what is constructive may be made to coincide with mine, as her boss.

Julie is an independent soul. She once jumped into a river to rescue a dog. Nothing wrong with that, you may say: a humanitarian act towards our dumb friends which deserves nothing but praise. Normally, yes, I would agree, but in this case our praise must be tempered with criticism, because before jumping into the river, Julie took off her dress. This not only meant that the poor pooch in

distress was put into greater danger as Julie wasted time disrobing before launching her rescue attempt, but much more importantly the entire image of the Leisure Centre was put at risk by Julie's naked leap into the swirling waters, in front of an eager audience who had gathered to watch the annual boat race regatta. 'Gym Girl in Topless Drama' screamed the local newspaper headlines. Julie's excuse that it was a brand new dress and she wasn't going to ruin it just doesn't hold water. The dog's grateful owner would have happily paid for a new dress to replace any destroyed by the corrosive action of our rivers, and he would not have had to avert his eyes in embarrassment as his dog was handed back safely. Nor would Julie have got paw marks on parts of her body where paw marks should not be found.

Weatherby, Colin is my Deputy Manager (Wet), and sometimes I wonder whether he is really cut out for a career in the leisure environment. He is keen, hard-working, devoted to all that Whitbury New Town Leisure Centre stands for, always keen to learn and a fully paid up subscriber to my Dream. Yet somehow he falls short of my ideal Deputy Manager (Wet). I know that Deputy Manager (Wet) is a difficult role to fulfil in even the best run Leisure Centres, such as Whitbury, because it involves constant supervision of the pool and all its related

activities, but even so, I sometimes wonder whether Colin will ever get to grips with it. Yet he feels he has found his niche here at Whitbury, and perhaps he has. If so, it is one of the most heavily infected niches I have ever come across.

There was a time when I wondered whether Colin's unfortunate allergies and ailments could be put down to Sick Building Syndrome, but I have decided this is not the case. It is just Sick Colin Syndrome. Having as a Deputy someone who is neither athletically perfect nor even basically sound of mind and limb is a challenge, but one of the basics tenets of good business practice is that there should be no discrimination against any candidate for any post simply on the grounds that he or she is entirely unsuitable for the job and incapable of carrying it out. If that were a criterion for job selection, where would most of you be? Down at the Job Centre with your P45s and with scarcely enough money to invest in life-enhancing publications like this one, that's where you would be.

Amazing to relate, Colin has a daughter. I first suspected that Colin had experienced the joys of fatherhood when he mentioned at a staff meeting that he thought I was right to insist on separating men and women at night. "That's when things happen, at night. That's when people get carried away. They start talking to someone, just to be friendly. They find they have a lot of shared interests, and as the evening goes on they get closer and closer."

"Yes. Thank you Colin," I said, trying to drag the meeting back from this discussion of the philosophy of love and loneliness to the matter at hand. But Colin was not to be deterred.

"They have a few drinks, because it's her birthday, perhaps. They stretch out on a gym mat, just to relax, and before you know it the court is ordering him to pay £14.70 a month maintenance for the next eighteen years. For example."

Call me intuitive if you like, but with my extraordinary feel for the inner perceptions of those around me, I was able to guess from this little outburst that Colin was not talking merely theoretically. He was speaking from experience. And £14.70 a month maintenance is not much. I think he was lucky that Stephanie's mum decided to emigrate to Australia. Stephanie's mum was lucky too, come to that...

Whistler, Tim is one of our footsoldiers, but a good man, nonetheless. He is, like all the others, a strong member of what I now believe is the best Leisure Industry support team in the Southern Area. He appears ever willing to co-operate, although he has a rather forced smile sometimes which I am sure would fool somebody less sensitive to these matters than me, but which occasionally leads me to wonder how much he has his heart in Leisure. Once, for instance,

Tim with Gavin

there was a little panic over the antenatal Class, and I had to ask one of the girls to lend a hand at short notice. I consulted my staff schedules to discover that this is turn meant that Tim had to be volunteered for pool duty. Of course, I realised it was his half day, but it was one of those times when all hands had to be on deck. Tim smiled in his usual cheery way when greeted with this slight change in his afternoon's plans, but when I pointed out that perhaps he was a little overdue for a fresh green T-shirt, as a courtesy to those who would be swimming in the pool, there was a definite frostiness in the smile. I can't understand that sort of attitude. It should be not only a pleasure but also second nature to a Leisure Industry executive to ensure that he (or she, although in Tim's case I know the girls will agree with me that he's all *he*) has a fresh T-shirt at all times. Appearing in a state of perfect neatness and freshness is one of the perks of the job (see DRESSING FOR SUCCESS below).

WHITBURY NEW TOWN LEISURE CENTRE

ORGANIZATIONAL CHART

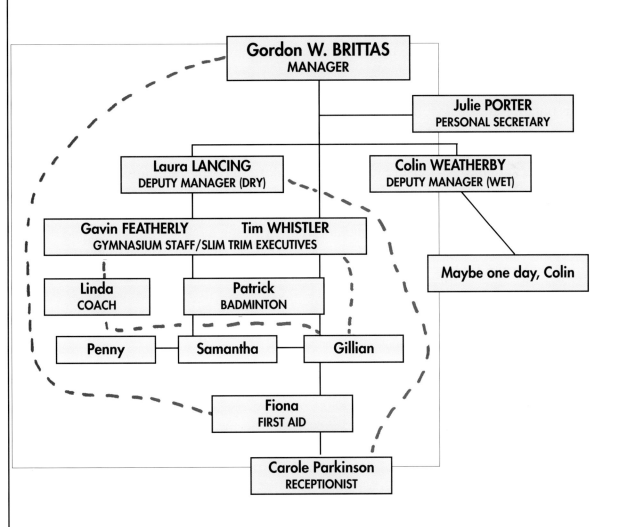

Note: Dotted line responsibilitry for pool attendance and pool cleaning exists between Gavin and Tim, Linda and Gillian. Straight line responsibility from the receptionexists between the Manager, Mr. Gordon W. Brittas and the receptionist, Ms Carole Parkinson, except that there is not room on the chart to draw a straight line.

COMPLAINTS

As I once remarked to a customer who seemed to be staring vacantly at one of our notice boards, "If you have got a complaint, put it in the box, just like everybody else." We have a perfectly good black metal box on the wall beside the notice board to take complaints. It is emptied every three hours, and every complaint is personally checked by myself, as Leisure Centre manager. I feel it is a very healthy sign that there are so many customer complaints, because it is a well known marketing rule (learnt by me by attending several seminars on the subject - see COURSES below) that a complaint is really a gesture of support. When a customer is so eager to ensure that his (or her) favourite product or service retains its reputation for quality, he (or she) will write a letter of complaint whenever he (or she) perceives a drop in quality, however minuscule that drop might be. This is not to criticise the provider of the service for that drop in quality, but merely to remind us at Whitbury Leisure Centre how important to the community are the facilities we provide, and how determined are the writers (or writeresses) of those complaints that the staff of the Centre, who are the custodians of the town's health and well-being, are always vigilant in maintaining a facility that is beyond reproach. We set ourselves high standards, and expect the community to keep us up to those standards.

That is why, for example, I complained to the Duchess of Kent about the piece of paper she dropped and suggested she pick it up. I am an ardent Royalist, as are all good Leisure Centre managers, so I am always concerned that the very highest standards are

**Pop it in the box.
What could be simpler?**

maintained by even the most minor members of that Family at all times. And that is also why I suggested that the Rotarians do their best to keep up their hard-won reputation for care in the community by using the Gents facilities properly. Not lifting the seat is hardly the kind of example a major charitable organisation like theirs wants to show to the rest of us, is it, even at their annual dinner? My action in giving the President a mop and a list of offenders was a gesture of support for the Rotary Club (Whitbury New Town chapter), and should not have been misinterpreted in the way it was. How can anybody expect even the most caring of complainers to continue with his support when his feet have been set in a bucket of concrete?

Anyway, it is particularly gratifying to learn that at Whitbury, we have the highest rate of complaints per customer in the entire country. No fewer that 3.42 letters of complaint per visit were received by us last year, including a petition containing 23,496 signatures (a total higher than the entire population of Whitbury, which shows what an impression we have made upon everyone in the area) asking why the Centre was closed for 174 days during the very same year. That particular complaint was easy to respond to: when the moral and physical health of the community is at stake, we cannot afford to take chances with, for example, Sick Building Syndrome or a propane gas explosion.

Other subjects of complaint range from the length of time that players are allowed to use the squash courts (there is a serious danger of heart attacks, exhaustion and other physical disadvantages if any but the fittest of our regulars try to play for longer than twenty minutes at a stretch, as I have told

Complaints received during the month of January – a reasonable response considering there were only seven signs advising customers of the location of the complaints box.

many people, in writing), the difficulties in deciphering a doctor's signature on the medical certificate required to become a member (so many are forged by people who do not take this sort of stringent but necessary medical pre-certification seriously), problems of Peeping Toms in the Ladies' changing rooms (actually this was a Peeping Colin, but it was entirely accidental and done in the best interests of our lady members), and the lack of places to hang shoe bags in the wake of the demolition of the building after the mishap with the fuel tanker.

Complaints received during the month of February – by now the customers were beginning to learn how the system works.

Complaints received during the month of March – proof enough that the complaints box system is a raving success and one of Whitbury Leisure Centre's most popular features.

CONTENTS

When I was informed by my editor, Humphrey Pratt of the Whitbury printing and Publicity Co. Ltd. that my book would require a page detailing its contents, I devoted days of research to produce the following charts. These demonstrate, in an interesting and stimulating manner, the exact content of this product broken down into its constituent elements.

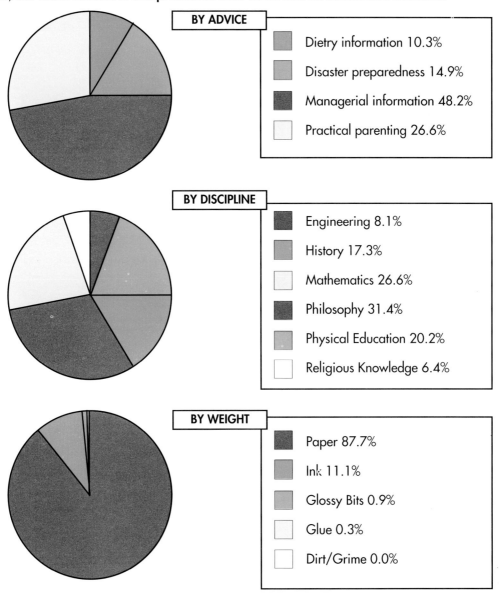

BY ADVICE

Dietry information 10.3%

Disaster preparedness 14.9%

Managerial information 48.2%

Practical parenting 26.6%

BY DISCIPLINE

Engineering 8.1%

History 17.3%

Mathematics 26.6%

Philosophy 31.4%

Physical Education 20.2%

Religious Knowledge 6.4%

BY WEIGHT

Paper 87.7%

Ink 11.1%

Glossy Bits 0.9%

Glue 0.3%

Dirt/Grime 0.0%

I was disturbed to discover later that all that was actually required was a list of subject headings and the page number on which they appear. Such communication breakdowns are the bane of effective management.

COURSES

I have, in the pusuit of my Dream, been on many different courses in my life, all of which are now detailed in a folder apiece on a shelf in my office, where they can be referred to at any time. Being properly trained for the job is important. Most courses try to teach us mundane skills like Word Processing or Accounting For The Innumerate. I remember that last year I went on a weekend computer course, and the bloke there actually taught us all how to program things. I am

NUMBER OF NEW COURSES INTRODUCED AT
WHITBURY LEISURE CENTRE

1995
1994
1993
1992
1991
1990
1989

10   15   20   25

NUMBER OF NEW COURSES

therefore now able to use all types of computers in all situations, and yet, somehow I prefer the familiarity of pencil and paper in calculating. Why is it that computers seems to bring out the very worst in people, creating needless aggression and aggravation every time anyone merely taps a few keys for fun? That's the sort of thing we need to learn on these courses, not just how to enter and exit by pressing a couple of mice. But anyway, I've been on enough courses myself to realise that the important thing is the giving of knowledge and experience, not the receiving of it. These days, I

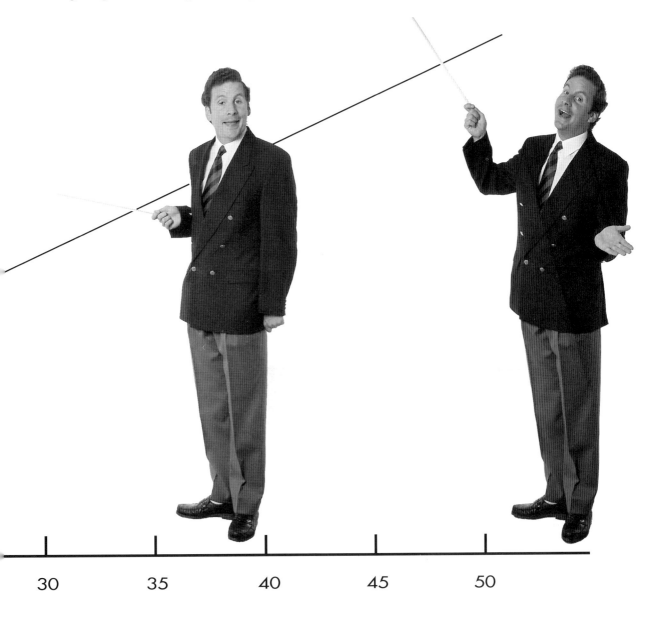

30   35   40   45   50

don't attend courses to learn. I leave that to others who still have a lot of growing, both physical and mental, to do before they are fully rounded human beings. I prefer to organise courses, so that I can pass on the Dream to those who will be our future.

Other people have business skills, and good luck to them, but my skill is people. I know how to deal with people. No course can teach a person people skills: you are either born with them or you are not.

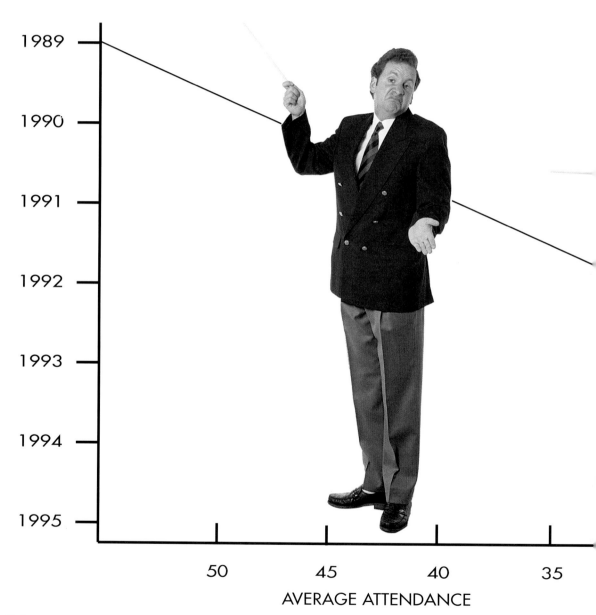

Thus it is that at Whitbury Leisure Centre, we run a wide variety of courses on a whole range of subjects of value to the community. Not all of them have been as well attended as I would have wished, but as I have said many times before and will say again many times in the future, we cannot judge the success of any event by the numbers that attend. All of our courses have added to the experience of sharing the dream with my fellow Whitbury folk, and thus they are all successes.

When Councillor Druggett forced me to resign from the management of the

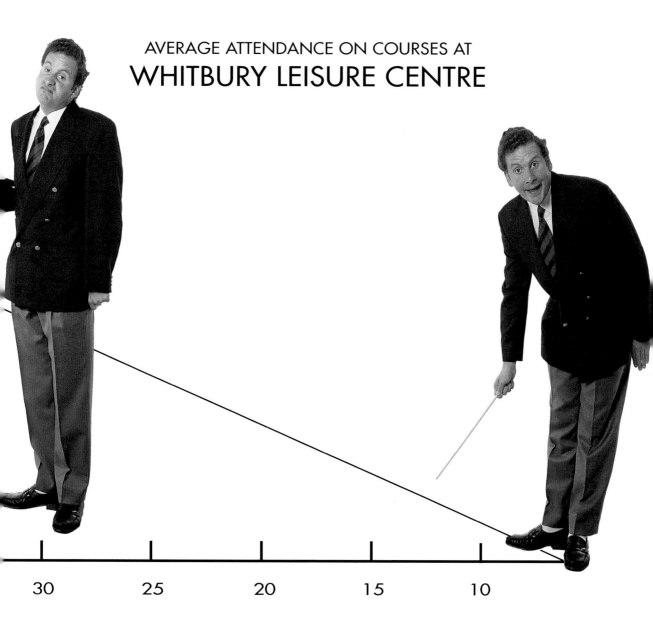

AVERAGE ATTENDANCE ON COURSES AT
WHITBURY LEISURE CENTRE

30   25   20   15   10

Centre, my replacement was a nice enough bloke called Alan Digby. Now, I found no personal fault with Al, who was doing his best to keep the Centre running, but I suspect that he found it was rather like trying to control a Formula One racing car when one has been driving a Ford Cortina for years. Nothing wrong with a Ford Cortina, of course, but a highly engineered sophisticated piece of equipment like a racing car or Whitbury Leisure Centre runs on different fuel. Poor Al failed to understand that my management style, which has kept Whitbury Leisure Centre running at an astonishing level of efficiency for so long, involves running many courses, and he even went so far as to cancel Colin's unusual course on Herbal Healing, just because nobody ever came. As Colin remarked to me at the time, "You always said the important thing was to be there," and he was right. The course exists: the course is part of the overall philosophy of the Centre: the course helps us to share the Dream. Therefore the course is a success, even if attendance figures are slightly lower than we might have hoped for. No wonder Al did not last long.

I could quote many more examples of the existence of the course being of more significance than the attendance levels. The fact that our Life Saving For The Elderly classes, for instance, were attended only by Colin, despite the fact that he is neither Elderly nor much of a swimmer, is no criticism of the classes: it is a criticism of the type of people who failed to sign up for the programme. Do the Elderly not realise that the ability to save lives in a swimming pool, or at least to be able to pick up a brick lying in eight feet of water, is a necessary skill during the ageing process?

WARNING
Pensioners diving practice,
Wednesday 9.30 am.

WARNING
Helpers beware! Old people
are slippery when wet!

WARNING
No colostomy
bags in pool.

WARNING
No pets in the pool
(except guide dogs).

Colin is now ready for his declining years (except that he failed to pick up the brick in anything more than two feet of water), but the old folk of Whitbury are not. For the management and staff of Whitbury Leisure Centre, that is not enough. These people must be interested in changing their entire lifestyles, to respect their bodies for all time, for the body is the temple of the soul.

My antenatal classes went rather better. I had to dismiss Mrs Lucas, who used to give these classes, as her attitude was wrong, but I felt that I was quickly able to overcome the objections of some of the ladies who attended the classes, including my darling Helen.

"You've dismissed the most popular ante-natal teacher in the whole of the South of England?" asked Helen, eager to understand the reasoning of senior management.

"Popular she may have been, my darling, but she was also sexist. How anyone in this day and age can believe that men should be excluded from the experience of pregnancy is beyond me. This is the Nineties, Helen. Childbirth is not a female experience. It's something we share."

WARNING
Maximum of two pregnant ladies in the pool at any one time due to excess water displacement.

WARNING
Congregating in reception is forbidden for those over six months gone. The obstruction caused constitutes a fire hazard.

WARNING
Giving birth underwater may be trendy but contravenes EC Pool Hygiene regulations.

WARNING
It is dangerous for pregnant ladies to rollerskate in the corridors.

I think my style of running this particular course added something to the experience of pregnancy that had until that moment been missing. Of course I kept Mrs Lucas' soothing background music, partly because nobody could find the switch to turn it off, but I was also able to bring the complete family, both male and female elements, into the occasion.

"While we're thinking these gentle positive thoughts, let's remember Dad. Because sometimes he gets left out, doesn't he? Let's remember Jim, eh, Brenda, and hope his worries over redundancy and the fall-off in the motor trade prove unfounded. Let's remember Bob, shall we Elaine? And we all hope you hear some news of him before too long."

That brought a particularly deep sigh, almost a sob, from Elaine. How satisfying to contribute positively to these ladies' biological experiences. Bob doesn't know what he's missing, living in Guildford over a newsagent with his secretary.

"And let's all try and forget that these are worrying times to be bringing a child into the world. We want to be positive and not think of all the many things that can go wrong with the actual birth itself – although we will be discussing one or two of those in next week's class."

CUSTOMERS

I don't like to think of the people who come to the Leisure Centre as 'customers'. It's so impersonal. I prefer to think of them as statistics. Statistics are not important to the realisation of the Dream. What counts is what is in one's heart.

It is difficult to understand why some of the people who do use the Leisure Centre come here at all. They don't seem to want to do anything more than just swim or play squash. They don't have any ulterior motivation. And they are thoughtless. I caught one man swinging his squash racket in the confined space of the changing rooms, and so as Manager, I felt it only right that I pointed out the error of his ways.

"Excuse me!" I shouted, quite politely. The man stopped. "Yes, you with the racket." Members of the public, although they are often entirely anonymous, like to feel they are being properly identified by those in authority over them. "I wonder if you realise exactly how dangerous that is?"

"What?" he replied, rather aggressively.

"Swinging a squash racket in a confined space. Supposing some small child came running in here looking for its father! You could have slammed it in the jaw and disfigured it for life." Squash players never think further ahead than their next serve.

"There's nobody here!"

He missed the point completely. "But there could have been. Statistics show there's one accident per year in a leisure centre with a squash racket."

"Oh do they really! Oh dear! Well, let's do our bit for safety, shall we?" With that he smashed his racket against the wall and broke it. "There! One accident with a squash racket. Now I suppose we can relax for the rest of the year, can't we!"

He went on the blacklist straight away. Apart from being the kind of disruptive influence that we do not want in the Centre, he also obviously has no grasp of the significance of statistics, which though unimportant to the realisation of the Dream, still need to be understood for what they are. One accident in a leisure centre per year with a squash racket doesn't mean that you can break a racket and thus be safe. How silly! It was mid-July when we had that particular discussion, so statistically we had already had about half an accident. His extra complete accident brought the yearly tally up to one and a half, with still over five months to go. What is more, it wasn't really an accident because it looked to me as though he did it on purpose. Anyway, I took the only precautionary course I could. I put up a notice on the notice board warning all members of the Leisure Centre to be aware that we had over-fulfilled our quota of squash racket accidents for the year, and that people should be extra vigilant as we were already eating into next year's

C

allocation. It was an awkward period, I can tell you.

Another problem I have with customers is that they do not understand my priorities. I cannot let them use the facilities when the Southern Area Inspectorate is about to call on us. I have to put the Cleaning Programme into effect. But there are some who do not understand this simple fact. One old man who was using the swimming pool all on his own, rather laboriously breast-stroking his way up and down the pool, seemed less than gracious when I offered him the chance to take a short break.

"Are you going to be much longer?" I asked him as he turned for his third length.

He stopped and held onto the side of the pool, showing his obvious lack of fitness. I would have expected a fit swimmer to keep himself afloat without having to hold onto the side.

"Well, I'm booked in for the next hour."

"Yes, I realise that." Always take the customer's side. It puts him at his ease. "It's just that we are rather anxious to sweep the pool and I wondered if you wouldn't mind sitting out on the other side for a while."

"Oh," said the old man. That was probably all he could manage after his exertions.

"Shouldn't take more than forty minutes, but it is rather important."

SWIMMING POOL USAGE TIMETABLE

DAY	FROM	TO	
WED	8.00	8.30	Morning pool clean. Pool closed.
	8.30	9.00	Changing/toilet facilities cleaning. Pool closed.
	9.00	9.30	Staff meeting. Pool closed.
	9.30	10.30	Cracked tile check. Pool closed.
	10.30	11.00	Staff tea break. Pool closed.
	11.00	11.30	Single Swimmers Special. Unmarried mothers only.
	11.30	12.00	Chlorine levels check. Pool closed.
	12.30	1.30	Staff swimming time. Pool closed to public.
	1.30	2.30	Pool closed for one hour to allow lunch to digest.
	2.30	3.30	Shallow end: Whitbury High Diving Club. Deep End: Whitbury Non-Swimmers Circle.
	3.30	4.30	Life Saving Class: Resuscitation Of Non-Swimmers.
	4.30	5.00	Check for manky towels/lost trunks. Pool closed.
	5.00		Poll closes for the day.

DREAM (THE)

As I remarked to the national press shortly after Whitbury Leisure Centre had been burnt to the ground, "Managing a Leisure Centre has to be one of the most satisfying jobs in the world. It's all I ever wanted to do. Help bring people together. It's my dream." Was it Martin Luther King who said, "All I have to do is Dream"? How right he was, for an American.

There are several kinds of dream. Colin rather unnecessarily spent time which could have been better spent supervising poolside activities recounting a dream he had had, in which he was an eagle.

LEISURE CENTRE LEVELLED

Whitbury Leisure Centre was totallydestroyed in a mysterious explosion earlier today. Manager Gordon Brittas emerged from the rubble a hero, leading a shocked group of survivors to safety. Mr Brittas had miraculously escaped serious injury despite having been trapped deep in the heart of the collapsing building.

One rescue worker described him as "an inspiration to us all. I'd attend a disaster every day if Mr .Brittas was involved.

"It was very upsetting," he said. "I was this eagle, but instead of soaring aloft in the clouds with all the other eagles, I was stuck on the ground because I had this mange under my feathers. I just want to find out what it means." Typical of Colin.

The kind of Dream I want to talk about is the type of plan for the future which is a Dream at the moment, but will surely become reality before too long. Since my younger twin brother Horatio and I were young children, we have held on to our Dream. Horatio, as befits a man ordained by the Church of England, is more prone to doubts about the Dream than I am, but we still share this same Dream. I remember once, as he sat in my office in the Leisure Centre shortly before he was due to take up a job in the Lebanon, ministering to the shot at..

"Now tell me if I'm talking out of turn," I said, "but I think it's time I reminded you of something. Of two young men, starting off in the world, one going to theological college, the other going to Loughborough College of Physical Education. They wrote down on a bit of paper what their aims in life were going to be."

"I know."

"I've still got my copy," I announced proudly, producing a neatly folded sheet of paper from my wallet. Horatio rather sheepishly pulled a dog-eared slip of paper from his own wallet.

DREAM (THE)

"On my paper it says, 'Working Towards The Dream.'" And it did on his too. We have simple aims, which can be summarised as follows:

1. Setting up of a World Government
2. Promoting Team Spirit
3. Building a Sense of Community and Belonging
4. The Abolition of Crime
5. Fairer Allocation of the World's Resources

Contemplating the Dream, items 1 to 5

These aims can be summarised in the simple phrase 'Body and Soul'. But they are fairly difficult tasks for just one man to cope with, so we agreed to share the work. I look after the physical side of our culture's development, while Horatio takes care of the spiritual side. Some of the aims fall in between the two, of course.

Ending war, for example, is both a physical and a spiritual task. It takes a certain amount of spiritual effort to persuade the leaders of the world that war is basically an incorrect policy, and Horatio's appointment as Dean of Beirut has certainly taken us forward in helping people understand the basic religious reasons why killing each other is a rather messy answer to our difficulties. But if people are not to go about killing each other any longer, what else is there for the young men of our world to do? This is where my job in charge of the physical side comes in. If we can provide constructive but still physically exhausting alternatives to mass killing and genocide, such as badminton competitions or free trampolining for the under tens, then we can divert people's attention away from the need to machine-gun those who don't necessarily agree with all our opinions. My goodness, if we all went around killing people we didn't like very much, there wouldn't be many of you left alive, would there!

And if you think dreams cannot come true, then let me tell you the story of Edward Barrett. I first met Mr. Barrett in the third cubicle along in the men's lavatories at Whitbury Leisure Centre. He did not look like a sportsman, which was particularly encouraging for us as we had recently been trying to bring the lame, the halt and the unfit into the Centre, and here was one of them. He looked more like a gangster, with dark glasses, a broken nose and a double-breasted pinstripe suit with wide lapels. He seemed to be searching for something, which, figuratively speaking, I was finally able to give him.

"Can I help at all?" I asked him. Of course, I knew I could help, because I am the Manager, but he did not know that when first we met.

"What?" Poor Eddie, so unfocused, so aimless and drifting. Giving him a physical goal turned out to give him a spiritual goal as well.

"I wondered if there was some sort of problem. If it's toilet paper, we do always keep a spare roll..." When searching a man's soul for the cause of his physical distemper, it is best to start with the small questions and work towards the bigger ones.

"No, I was just... erm... I'm fine."

No, he was not just fine, but then inspiration struck me. "Excuse me! You're not Edward Barrett by any chance, are you?"

"Why?"

"I knew it! You're the one who's holding up my squash competition!"

6. A Religious Revival
7. The End of War
8. The Abolition of Poverty
9. Bringing People Together
10. Ending Cultural Differences

Contemplating
the Dream,
items 6 to 10

"I didn't know I was in a competition." That could be the answer given by every person who has failed in life. "I didn't know I was in a competition." Life is a competition, and I for one know that I am in it, well and truly in it. Up to here.

"If you'd read your original application form, you'd have noticed that you were automatically entered when you joined the Centre. You're in the final."

"I'm in the final? How did I get in the final?"

"You've been rather lucky, haven't you? You had some byes in the earlier rounds. And in some of the later rounds by the look of it."

You could see Eddie was pleased. "The final! Here, that's not bad, is it?" And off he went to play the most important squash game of his career thus far.

Presenting the Whitbury New Town Squash Champions Trophy to Eddie was one of the high points of my life.

"Fairly won, Mr. Barrett," I said. "My congratulations." I always think that short speeches are the best at times like these (see PUBLIC SPEAKING below).

"And I can keep it?"

"Take it home, put it on the mantelpiece, build a little display cabinet for it."

It was at this point that I changed several lives by implanting a seed in Eddie's subconscious. "Here you are, the town's champion squash player. I wonder if you have ever thought of using that position to help others. I mean, it's all very easy for us, with our cosy middle class lives, Edward. But we have to remember not all the kids out there have the advantages of you and me."

"Eh?"

"If we could just bring them in here, and with champions like you to attract them I know we could, can you imagine what miracles might happen?"

"Miracles..." Eddie was not one for making long speeches.

"The smile on the face of a child, when he takes those first hesitant strokes across the pool; the look on someone's face when they win a trophy for the first time and realise that life's a little bit more than hanging round street corners, getting involved in drugs and petty crime... You see what I mean?"

"Oh, yeah."

"It can happen, Edward. But we need you to help. Think not what your Leisure Centre can do for you, but rather what you can do for your Leisure Centre. I have this dream; a dream that leisure centres all over the land will bring people together through sport, eliminating at a stroke poverty, war, religious and cultural differences, and promoting team spirit and a fairer allocation of the world's resources. It's all a question of inner certainty. Whatever happens, you have to hold on to the things inside you, you have to hold on to the dream."

It was only a few months later, as I was about to be sentenced to seventeen

consecutive life sentences for murder and various other misunderstandings, that Eddie proved that the Dream is worth holding onto. Regardless of his own safety, he entered the witness box at what I must admit was an unnervingly late stage and at long last proved that he was not always a man of few words.

"I suppose I should have come forward before this, but I was scared of going to prison for twenty years, or of being murdered by my gang mates, but I can't hide any more. I cannot stand by and see an innocent man suffer. Not after what he's given me. He's given me a sense of worth as a human being. He's given me dignity. He's given me the knowledge that I don't have to spend the rest of my life in the gutter. That I can use my talents to help others."

He turned towards the jury who were as enthralled as any of us by the fervour of Eddie's testimony. "I have spent the last six months in a leisure centre in Wincanton, teaching small children to swim, coaching adolescents at badminton, helping others find the self-fulfilment that this man offered me. He showed me what life can be like. He has given me... well, he's given me a Dream." I could not have put it better myself.

Some months ago a strange bloke called Alan Matthews was ushered into my office. He was a doctor of some sort, and tried to to say that my staff were under stress. He felt that the cause of it was that, and here I quote this Matthews man, "Dreams can be dangerous. I sometimes think we'd be better off without them."

How he could have reached the exalted rank of doctor when he quite clearly failed to understand the basic purpose of life, I do not know. I hope that he could read the surprise and disdain in my voice when I reacted to this heretical outburst of his.

"But you've got to have a Dream! If you don't have a Dream, how you gonna make a Dream come true?"

"You see, if you forgot about world peace (see WORLD PEACE below) and fostering the brotherhood of man," he stammered, "and just ran a sports centre, I think everything would be fine."

"But what if I'm right? What if my Dream is a good Dream that really will help people?"

"It's always possible", said the doctor weakly. "I don't have all the answers, Mr. Brittas."

"But I do, you see. That's why I'm the Manager."

Having narrowly avoided seventeen consecutive life sentences for murder, my attempts to Share the Dream with the judiciary were in vain.

DRESSING FOR SUCCESS

There is little doubt that my appearance alone is often enough to create considerable reaction among my staff, even before I have made my opening remarks at whichever daily meeting it may be. This is because appearances are not deceptive. One must learn how to dress properly. I believe that clothes tell us

When he dressed up as me, Colin's passable impersonation of a Leisure Centre Manager might have fooled anyone with no sense of smell.

much of the man. Or woman, of course. A navy blazer with gold buttons, a pair of grey trousers and smartly polished black leather shoes, coupled with a bold yet somehow understated tie gives me that perfect sense of well-being which is so important for a successful Leisure Centre Manager.

Cleaning shoes is a relaxing pastime that I often engage in at times of tension. To be able to sit at the kitchen table, my jacket hung over the back of a chair and the shoe cleaning kit spread out before me, with the first of eight or nine pairs of leather and suede shoes to be brought back to a pristine condition - that is the way to forget about the cares of the world. Just sing a little song as you brush (I find that the rhythm of 'I Know An Old Lady Who Swallowed A Fly' is in perfect time with the regular swing of my right arm), and your troubles slip away.

Sir John Harvey-Jones　　　　**Richard Branson**　　　　**Michael Heseltine**

A successful manager needs a successful haircut. Hair should be neatly trimmed and combed at regular intervals throughout the working day. The three businessmen above, whilst having enjoyed a modicum of success, could go much further with a proper haircut.

My staff do not always follow my dress guidelines, which is, of course, one of the many reasons why they are still the staff and I am the Manager. When Laura was due to be interviewed for the position of Leisure Centre Manager at Teddington, I was able to take time to give her sound advice on how to look, even though I was enormously busy rehearsing my speech of welcome for the Member of Parliament for Truro, the Honourable Sebastian Coe. A good manager is never too busy to help a young colleague struggling up the ladder of promotion.

"Wear something smart," I told her. "Something that suits you. And possibly a dash of lipstick? Make yourself more attractive." It boosts confidence, you see.

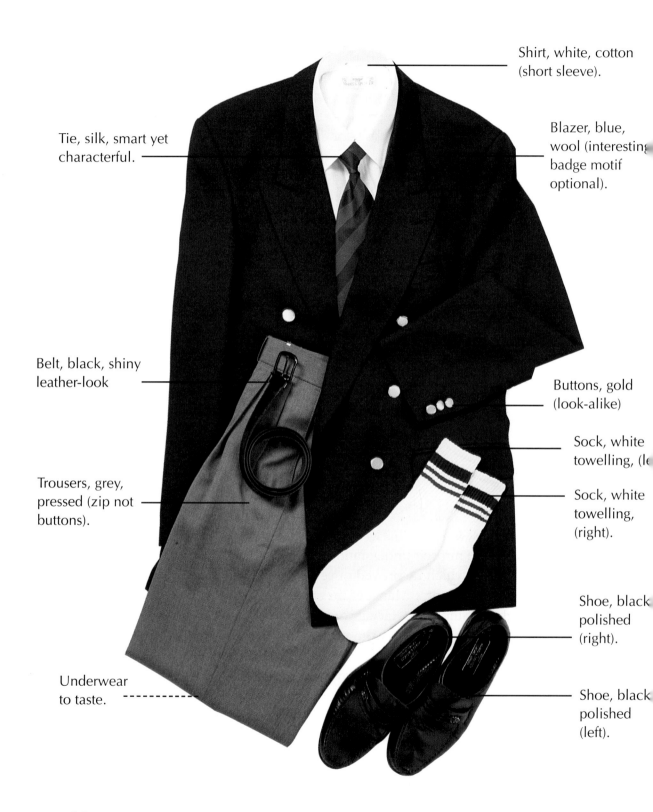

Shirt, white, cotton (short sleeve).

Blazer, blue, wool (interesting badge motif optional).

Tie, silk, smart yet characterful.

Belt, black, shiny leather-look

Buttons, gold (look-alike)

Sock, white towelling, (le

Sock, white towelling, (right).

Trousers, grey, pressed (zip not buttons).

Shoe, black polished (right).

Underwear to taste.

Shoe, black polished (left).

There's no point in looking dowdy, as Laura does tend to do sometimes. And before an interview, she must have had plenty to panic about already.

The rest of my staff are not likely to feature in anyone's list of best dressed people. Gavin, Tim, Linda and Patrick look fine in their shorts and Leisure Centre shirts, but Colin remains a problem. I well remember the occasion I had to point out to him that the Palace of Westminster was open, and all Colin did was look around him in blank amazement. What is the point in my asking our public to observe the basic standards of modesty in their dress if my staff cannot even take the time to button their flies? Colin tried to explain the fact that his shirt was poking through the entrance to his trousers by giving me the entirely unnecessary information that he had put rather a large rhubarb poultice on a delicately placed boil, and the strain of this extra bulk within his underwear had burst the zip. And I could persuade nobody to lend him a pair, so Colin remained at the leading edge of our laws of indecent exposure for the rest of the day.

Colin's general lack of understanding in matters of personal appearance, combined with an over-abundance of wax in his ears, did once cause some difficulties with the aforementioned Member of Parliament for Truro, the Honourable Sebastian Coe. A blue track suit is just not the same thing as a blue suit, so it was really unforgiveable that Colin should have chained the Honourable Mr. Coe, clad in a smart regulation Conservative party suit, to the side rail of the stairs in the corridor instead of an eight year old boy, wearing a blue track suit, who was under citizen's arrest for attempting to gain admission to the swimming pool without paying the requisite fee. Yet this is a man who can tell the difference between the dress of the tenth Roman legion and that of a group of Parthian mercenaries, just by one glance at the hordes who were besieging the Leisure centre at the time.

So Colin can make himself understand the meaning of dressing properly when he wants to, a quality which he proved once again when he attempted to impersonate a Leisure Centre Manager, in order to impress his long lost Australian daughter, Stephanie. He arrived at the Centre, on a day when he thought I would be away sailing with my family, wearing a blazer and tie, smart trousers, polished shoes and had even combed his hair. Somehow he had also contrived to lose his paunch. If a man like Colin, whose more usual look is of one who has spent the last six weeks living in a box under a motorway flyover, can appreciate that a neat appearance is the first step to social and commercial success, then how much easier is it for those of you who do not get your complete wardrobe from the War On Want shop in the High Street? Dress for success, and success will be yours.

EAT DRINK AND BE PERFECT

We must all take particular care with our diet. The great writer who gave us the lines, "Call my baby Lollipop, tell you why. His kiss is sweeter than apple pie," was touching an age old truth. We are what we eat, a fact which is proved by the French eating snails and horses and the Japanese making a speciality out of the

GOOD diet
Organically
Regulates
Digestion
Of
Nutriment

contents of a sea-cucumber's stomach.

A properly balanced diet is an essential part of any healthy lifestyle. As a Leisure Centre Manager, I have an obligation to society to keep my body in perfect condition, which of course would be impossible if I indulged in cream buns and hamburgers at every mealtime. The human body is a temple, as I find myself regularly needing to remind

E

BAD diet
Results
In
Tummy
Troubles
And
Smells.

my staff, and once we corrupt that temple by not giving it proper respect, we downgrade our whole purpose in being here. One of my little tricks to keep my own staff from not over-indulging is the lunchtime staff meeting. Of course, the staff meeting is absolutely vital to the smooth running of Whitbury New Town Leisure Centre, but I must confess that it is not absolutely vital that I hold it at lunch time. I do this partly in an attempt to make sure that nobody overeats in the middle of the day. .

We have our own restaurant at the Centre. Helen seems to spend a lot of her time there, eating doughnuts and drinking the coffee, (she should refer to the Time Management section of this book, as she does seem to spend too much of her life just hanging around waiting for me), but it does offer a full range of dishes for the dietarily aware. Fortunately, most of my staff are dietarily aware. Julie

knows not to order anything with fish in it from our restaurant, and Colin has at long last discovered that one of the things he is allergic to is yeast, whether taken internally as a foodstuff or externally as a poultice.

What is so good about eating is that you do not have to stick to the same sort of thing all the time. I am slightly suspicious of vegetarians and vegans and all that sort of thing, not because vegetarianism is crankish, which frankly it is - I mean all those straggly bearded people in horn rimmed glasses and open toed sandals telling the rest of us we should not enjoy the occasional sausage or barbecued steak - but because it makes life so difficult for the rest of us, we normal people who realise that man is an omnivore and will eat anything.

But I am never one to be unsympathetic towards the foibles of other people. In a spirit of caring for others and respecting their ideals, however silly they may appear to be, we at Whitbury Leisure Centre have a number of purpose designed forms that vegetarians and vegans are asked to fill in, in duplicate and before eleven o'clock in the morning of the day preceding their proposed meal, if they wish our kitchens to meet their special faddish dietary requirements. It saves confusion in the long run.

Laura, on the other hand, is a good cook. It's not that I want her to find the way to my heart, although I suspect she is carrying a candle for me just a little, but when Helen goes away on holiday I have sometimes been invited round to Laura's little house for an evening snack. She makes excellent omelettes. I like to visit Laura's home when Helen is away, simply because I cannot bring myself to eat often in public restaurants. The standard of service these days is not good, and I find that the waiters do not have the sense of deference towards their customers that once was taken for granted in England's best restaurants. Nowadays, whenever a diner tries to give a little friendly advice to a waiter, about the cleanliness of the tablecloth or perhaps how to take down our orders

---

WHITBURY LEISURE CENTRE RESTUARANT
MENU

When you eat and when you ride,
keep your elbows by your side

SOUP
(of the day)

FISH
(of the day)

CHICKEN
(of the day)

CURRIED CHICKEN
(of yesterday)

JAM ROLY POLY
(only available to customers with an
"I've Reached My Ideal Weight/Height Certificate")

PRUNES

N.B. Food will not be served to anyone who cannot produce a valid "I've Washed My Hands" slip signed by a member of staff.

by starting with the senior lady and working back anticlockwise to the host, instead of bowing deferentially and saying, "Yes, sir. Of course, sir", as any well-trained waiter should, they take every comment as a personal insult and go on the rampage, hurling abuse and mulligatawny soup at the unfortunate diner. I have learnt never to order lobster thermidor, now that waiters have discovered how to create maximum discomfort to the diner as they stuff it down his shirt front, and I have come to realise how difficult it is to get rid of both the stain and the smell of a blue cheese Ploughman's lunch when it hits your shirt from thirty paces. I can never understand how such aggressive waiters can hold on to their job for more than a few days, but I take it as a sign of the sad decline in standards of service throughout society today.

ATTENTION

Specially trained staff are on hand at all times in this facility should any customer require the use of a stomach pump.

The telephone number for Whitbury Hospital Accident and Emergency Unit is available from reception on production of a restaurant receipt and a fully completed "Symptoms of Sickness" form WLC IIIA/d.

What is more, for this amazing lack of service, they expect to charge us the earth. Like all normal people, I check the bill at restaurants very carefully, and it never ceases to amaze me the prices they think they can charge for items that haven't even been consumed. As I said to one restaurant manager just before he started poking me in the ribs, you can't charge more for two brandies than it would cost me to teach three disabled children to swim, especially when the second brandy was not even completely drunk. We all knew they were going to pour it back into the bottle, just as they were going to serve up the uneaten rolls again the next night. If I'd had a dog, I'd have asked for a doggy bag, but even the sort of dog that Helen would go for would probably draw the line at stale rolls and overpriced brandy.

FITNESS AND FIGURE TARGETS

F

One of our responsibilities as Leisure Industry executives is to show by example how much more attractive it is to have a body glowing with health and fitness than one which merely hangs limply from the owner's skeleton and wobbles. We want people to come here and say, "Oh look at the physique on that young person! I wish I looked like that."

But it occurred to me one day that this is probably not what people say. Do my team have the bodies that other people really want? I looked around the staff room during one lunchtime staff meeting and, being as honest with myself as I could, I'm afraid I had to answer my own question in the negative. "No, we do not, thank you very much." I therefore established my programme of Individual Fitness and Figure Targets for each member of my team.

They took me three months to put together, three long months of late nights with the developer tray in the dark room and my pocket calculator and my multi-coloured Whitbury New Town Leisure Centre Ball Point Pen, which leaks despite assurances from the suppliers, Whitbury Printing and Publicity Co. Ltd., that it would not. Within each Individual Fitness and Figure Target file I listed not only some general Dos and Don'ts, but also a personalised programme of diet, exercise and mental discipline that would take each and every member of my team, over a six month period, to a peak of physical well-being. Except for Carole's. Hers was a two year outline.

It was all very simply laid out. On page one, there was a photograph of the fileholder's physical condition as it was at the start of the programme, over which I had prepared a plastic overlay to highlight the areas in need of attention. Getting the photographs was no problem. With the aid of the local video shop, I was able to transfer tape from the security cameras in the changing rooms onto a still frame, thus obtaining the necessary 'Before' portrait to use as a starting point for the programme.

**WARNING: The overweight should not attempt to excercise unsupervised.
Trying to touch your toes is dangerous, especially if you haven't seen them for a while.**

FITNESS AND FIGURE TARGETS

Everybody seemed quite excited about the programmes when I introduced them. They caused a lot of lively comment and strong feelings were aroused, which I suppose was not surprising. It was the kind of thoughtful idea to help them all get fitter and healthier that they had come to expect from me as their Manager. I must confess that I never really found out how well these programmes worked, and how they had helped my team to come to terms with their bodies, as it was at about that time they sent me to Coventry for several weeks, and they were thus unable to tell me how much better they were feeling.

Before: Had I not been blessed with a will of iron, three sugars in my tea instead of one and a half might, over the years, have left me like this – in need of an individual Fitness and Figure Target.

After: Since I am almost a perfect weight for my body type, height, bone structure, age, hairstyle and shoe size, I am my own Individual Fitness and Figure Target.

FLIP CHARTS AND NOTICE BOARDS AND THEIR USE IN LEISURE CENTRES

F

I cannot conceive of running a Leisure Centre, or at least not one with such an influence on the physical and mental well-being of the local community as Whitbury's, without a regular supply of flip charts, complete with coloured pens and sticky tape. As for notice boards, a tidy notice board does more than let Joe Public (and Josephine Public, of course. And Ashraf and Sharmila Public) know what's on offer - much more. Notice boards are, as I have often remarked, the window to the soul of any Leisure Centre. So we must always make sure that they all have matching drawing pins and are all hung absolutely straight, and not at that slight angle that can be oh-so-irritating.

I find I use about ten flip charts a week. Each lunchtime staff meeting tends to take up one complete chart, expounding on the theories of a new timetable, or

explaining the difference between a highboard swallow dive with double tuck (degree of difficulty 2.2) and a forward one and half somersaults with three twists (degree of difficulty 2.8), which are of course quite difficult for some of my staff to grasp, but which still need to be fully understood by any member of the team.

Then there are notices to the general public, which I like to put up not only on the notice boards but also in places where they will really be seen. The blacklist of children banned from the centre, for example, is posted in both changing rooms and by the footbaths near the swimming pool. The full names and addresses of their parents are also added.

When we were fund raising for the new trampoline, I went on a sponsored silence. However, I still had a Leisure Centre to run even if I was not talking. Silence is golden, but my eyes still see.

I used my notice board skills to come up with a range of hand held signs which would cover almost any eventuality of a normal day at the office. There was

GOOD MORNING HOW CAN I HELP YOU?

and

I AM THE MANAGER. I'M SORRY I CAN'T TALK,
I'M ON A SPONSORED SILENCE

helped me to explain why I was using the cards, although there was no room for

IN AID OF OUR TRAMPOLINE

which had to go onto a separate card. I had other cards which read

LEAVE IT TO ME. I'LL DEAL WITH IT

and

BACK IN TWO MINUTES,

which seemed to cover most problems. I think it is a good management exercise to create these cards, even if one is not on a sponsored silence, to enable you to identify those situations which occur most often at work, and to see whether or not changes to the style of working are advisable. In my case, I proved to my own satisfaction that no changes were needed. The cards stating

JUST DO IT, COLIN

got rather grubby from overuse by about lunchtime, but I found the triple combination of

AND WHERE DO YOU THINK YOU ARE GOING?

followed immediately by

DO YOU HAVE ANY FORM OF IDENTIFICATION?

and then

I'M AFRAID I MUST ASK YOU TO LEAVE

sorted out just about every problem that the day could throw at me.

GAME OF LIFE (THE)

Life is a game, and you have to understand how to play it if you want to succeed. So I have invented the Gordon Brittas Game Of Life, to help everybody win. Well, that's not strictly true, because in my Game there is only one winner and several losers, but that is the same in life itself, and the Game will help us come to terms with our deficiencies and realise that a loser is a loser whatever the circumstances. Anyway, the game took me a great deal of thought and time to design, so let's just get on with it.

The Rules of my Game are simple, so simple that they could be written up in a 36 page booklet, if you use small print and provide each player with a magnifying glass. Otherwise, it's a 900 page shelf bender, complete with illustrations.

Let me summarise the basic rules:

● **1.** Before the game begins, each player must be in possession of (a) a Rule Book, (b) a Badge signifying whether the player is a Wise Virgin (WV) or a Foolish Virgin (FV), (c) a scorepad and (d) a pencil (not a ballpoint pen: it may leak and stain the board).

● **2.** The Wise Virgins have to give the Banker £1,500 before the game starts and on every circuit of the board. This money is invested by the Banker in a Personally Managed Pension Fund for each Wise Virgin.

● **3.** The Foolish Virgins make no such preparation for the future.

● **4.** Every player, whether Wise or Foolish, is also given three starting cards. These cards show the players' Aptitudes, Genetic Heritage and Socio-Economic Background, summarising the balance between Nature and Nurture that affects us all. So, it may be that your Aptitude Card says 'Good at Languages' or 'Musically Talented' or (the worst of all) 'No Ball Sense'. Your Genetic Heritage card will say 'Short and Fat' or 'Prone to Coronary Disease' or 'Asthmatic and Twitchy', while your Socio-Economic Background card will reveal whether you are an aristocrat, of upper middle-class stock but living in genteel poverty, or a C2 or D tattooed navvy.

● **5.** As in the real Game of Life, you have to throw a six to start.

● **6.** Then you make your way round the board and every time you pass 'Go', which represents another year, you take your salary and three more cards. These are a Career Card, to see whether or not you've been promoted or made redundant; your Family Card, to see whether you have got divorced or anything like that; and of course your Catastrophe Card.

When I explained this annual three card experience to Laura, she wondered whether it was necessary to suffer a Catastrophe every year. "Tragic but true", I replied. It is important to keep the Game as close as possible to the real thing, so that real lessons can be learnt. And where would we be if we tried to pretend that Catastrophes do not happen annually. Or more frequently.

Here is a typical Catastrophe Card.

> ## CATASTROPHE CARD
> You lose a limb in an industrial accident and are unable to work. Lose your job and go back four squares.

The Career Cards have true to life messages such as 'You have been turned down for promotion again - lose six months' salary and take a Fortune Card.' And the Fortune Cards reflect the harsh realities of life with statements like, 'Housing market collapses. Flat repossessed. Go back to the bedsitter.' Of course, as the years pass and the cleverer players get richer, there are devices for avoiding some of the worst pitfalls in the Game Of Life. Buying a car allows you to hop over every third red square - the squares with the Fortune Cards - and sending your children to a private school gives them advantages when they come to be issued Socio-Economic Cards and Aptitude Cards in their own game. They can then look after you in your old age, even if the Personal Pension Plan taken out by the Wise Virgins has not matured successfully.

When I invited my staff to play the Game, young Timothy decided by the end of the game that it did not work properly. "It doesn't work. I'm doing all the sensible things like working hard and saving money, and I'm just getting worse and worse off, whereas Gavin there is spending money like water and he's as rich as Croesus. It's not fair."

My reply was immediate. "That's life for you, Tim. Life is not fair. It never has been. In real life, it doesn't matter how hard you work or what you believe in, it's all based on luck. You work hard, you give it everything you've got, but at the end of the day all you actually do is roll a dice. You roll the right number and you succeed beyond your wildest dreams. Throw another number and it all goes down the sewer."

Gavin, the winner, was impressed. "That's quite a clever game, Mr. Brittas."

"Oh, it's clever all right, Gavin. But it doesn't mean to say people don't get hurt."

GORDON OF KHARTOUM

My father named me after one of his heroes, the soldier and
Imperialist, Charles George Gordon (1833 - 1885). Gordon entered
the Royal Engineers at the age of 19, and fought in the Crimean War

Gordon of Khartoum in a potentially tricky situation.

in 1855 and took part in the Chinese Expedition of 1860. He also helped the Chinese government of the time suppress the Taeping Rebellion of 1863 and 1864, which earned him the popular soubriquet 'Chinese Gordon'. I don't think that I am inscrutable enough, or indeed as yellow-skinned and fluent with the Mandarin tongue, ever to be known as Chinese Gordon Brittas. Still, I keep his picture on my office wall and try to live up to his example.

In 1873 he went off to the Egyptian Sudan and was Governor there between 1877 and 1880. In 1885 he was holed up in Khartoum, surrounded by the forces of somebody called the Mahdi, who duly stormed his defences and killed him just two days before his birthday. That was very bad luck.

According to the 'Martial Arts' section of my Encyclopaedia Of The Leisure Industry, Gordon was "a soldier of true heroic type, a mediaeval warrior saint, a puritan mystic in the midst of 19th century materialism." He was a man who, left to himself, repeatedly accomplished the apparently impossible chiefly through his own extraordinary power of influencing others. He never went back on his word. During the final stages of the siege in Khartoum, he put out an order rationing the water supply, and this little lad, one of his favourite servants, Abdul his name was, stole a saucerful of water for his dying puppy. Old Gordon had a soft spot for Abdul but he couldn't go back on his word and, although the lad was only nine years old, he was court- marshalled and shot.

Mind you, the whole lot of them were dead a few days later, so it didn't make much difference to Abdul's life expectancy. Nor the puppy's.

Gordon had a Dream, rather like me. I remember his life was serialised in picture form in the Eagle comic when I was a lad.

You can see the similarity, although rather than brandish a firearm I believe the rampaging hordes may have responded more positively to my assertive pose and stern look.

HONESTY

I remember once remarking to Gavin, "You may one day learn, young Gavin Featherly, that not everyone in this world is as honest as you or I." This was on the occasion when I was inspecting behind the cistern in the third cubicle in the gents' lavatories, and found a key. It turned out to be the key to a locker in which had been placed a black briefcase, which contained £650,000 in £10 notes. Some would say that it would have been easier to have left the key hidden where it was, and then perhaps I would not have found myself in court facing six charges of murder, four charges of grievous bodily harm and one of possessing controlled drugs, in contravention of Section 4 of the Misuse of Drugs Act 1971. However, that is taking the easy way out. There is sometimes a price to pay for being honest, but it is a price we have to pay if we are to live at ease with ourselves and welcome each new day with an easy conscience.

Ask anybody what they think of me, and they will say I'm hardworking, honest and trustworthy. They may add other adjectives to that list as well, but that does not worry me. As long as the words 'honest' and 'trustworthy' are up there with

THE EIGHT VIRTUES by Gordon Brittas

1.	HONESTY	Always tell the truth, even when it hurts, and never borrow a Leisure Centre biro without signing for it.
2.	PATIENCE	'You can't hurry love, you'll just have to wait,' said the wise man. You can't hurry Colin, either.
3.	CLEANLINESS	Next to Godliness, except on this list.
4.	RESPECT FOR MANAGEMENT	Everybody must know their place in life.
5.	FORESIGHT	A little planning never hurt anybody (except for the extremely well-planned Battle of Trafalgar, 1805; that hurt quite a lot of people).
6.	TACT	This virtue can sometimes clash with Honesty (see above).
7.	COLOUR CO-ORDINATION	Red and Green should never be seen. But navy blue and grey goes with anything.
8.	HAVING A DREAM	John Lennon, Martin Luther King, Bing Crosby - all the great men of our age had dreams. Bing Crosby's was only of a white Christmas, of course, but any dream will do.

Julie's revelations may have been honest, but were they in the best interests of all concerned? She has much to learn.

the best of them, how can I feel that I am being misrepresented? One of the abiding principles of my life is a belief that the greatest of all the Eight Virtues is Honesty. I have heard Timothy suggest to Julie that I do not even know what the other Seven Virtues are, but that is neither here nor there. The greatest of them all is Honesty, so what does it matter what the others are? I think Patience is one of them. And Cleanliness.

So many people think that telling the truth is something you only have to do when it suits you, and that it is somehow all right to tell lies to get yourself out of trouble. But it never works. Of course, one of the problems with honesty is that sometimes people do not recognise the truth when they see it and hear it, which makes it difficult for the few of us who remain committed to a policy of absolute honesty at all times.

My secretary Julie knows where I stand on this. I know her heart was in the right place, even if her mouth let her down, when she told me what she had told Councillor Drugget. "I said that everyone knew you were a berk, but that you were an honest berk." I have a feeling that another of the Eight Virtues is Respect for Management, and if so, Julie Porter has some way to go before she can truly be described as virtuous. Jack Drugget, a man with whom I find I have little in common despite once casting my vote for his party in the local elections, was at the time attempting to find some small financial irregularity in the running of the Leisure Centre, with a view to using that as grounds for dismissing me. I have had enough brushes with the Angel of Unemployment to know that a lack of honesty is something no employer can tolerate, but something which no employer has yet accused me of. Successfully.

My dear Helen is, I am afraid, rather a different matter. When she is pregnant, she gets a primeval urge to shoplift, and this can be awkward when one is dealing with store managers who cannot distinguish between mere light fingers on the one hand and uncontrollable maternal instincts on the other. But she only has seven convictions, which is not the record of a career burglar, just a confused mother.

Helen about to give birth in the High Street surrounded by Whitbury's most tempting retail establishments but fortunately too preoccupied to indulge in a shoplifting spree.

HORATIO, VISCOUNT NELSON

My brother Horatio was named after one of my father's great heroes, the sailor and Imperialist, Horatio Nelson (1758 - 1805). I am not sure that there are many great similarities between Horatio and his namesake. For example, my brother still has both his arms and both his eyes, and has not yet begun a tempestuous affair with the wife of the British Minister in Naples. I have never heard him utter the words, "a peerage or Westminster Abbey" either. However, he does realise that England expects that every man will do his duty, and he tries hard to live up to that ideal.

In a way, I ought to have been called Horatio, if I was not already called Gordon. Actually, of course, since Horatio and I are twins I was not already called Gordon when Horatio was born. We were christened at the same time, although I, as the elder by twenty three minutes, was the first in the font. Still, if the vicar had made a mistake, I would have been Horatio and Horatio would have been Gordon. Anyway, the reason that the name Horatio would have suited me is that "Nelson's genius lay in his combination of energy, knowledge and judgement", it says here in the 'Boating' section of my Encyclopaedia Of The Leisure Industry. Sounds rather like me. "His decisiveness, personal magnetism, affection for his subordinates and sympathy for his seamen, as well as his magnificent bravery made him one of the supreme leaders of men. He was loved by those he commanded". Just like me.

I remember his life was serialised in picture form in the Eagle comic when I was a lad.

Nelson: noble, heroic, determined, inspired.

Me: ditto.

60

HOW TO RECOGNISE SUCCESS

The sweet smell of success is something we can all savour, because it is all about us. But we will be able to breathe in the heady perfume only if we know where success grows, for, as a wise man once wrote, "Success is more than climbing the mountain; it is in understanding which mountain to climb." We all have our own targets to hit and our own goals to score. Success is in scoring our own goals, not in foolishly trying to score for somebody else. Success need not be expressed in monetary terms, despite the views of many of those who visit my Centre, and indeed the views of some of those who work in it.

Michael T. Farrell III is not my favourite man, partly because he is married to Laura, who despite being on the verge of being too old, could have done better for herself; after all, as I have told her more than once, she's intelligent, quite attractive and fairly neatly turned out. But the main reason why Michael T. Farrell III is not my favourite man is because he thinks that money solves all problems.

When we were fund raising for a second trampoline so that we could offer synchronised trampolining, which is, as everybody knows, an essential part of growing into being a major Leisure Centre, he took all the fun out of it by just giving us the rest of the £2,500 we needed to raise – £2,495, I think it was. Gavin, Julie and Carole seemed to think it was good news that we suddenly had the money, so I had to put them right.

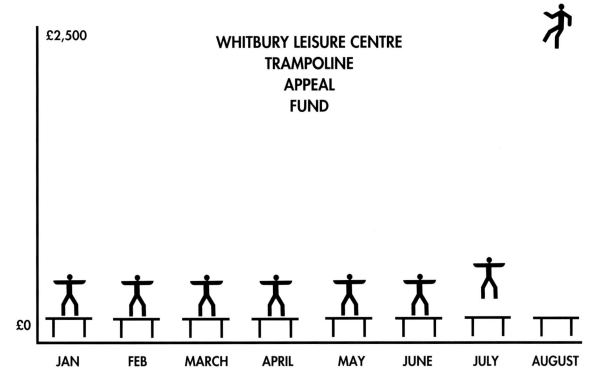

My regular talks and occasional less formal chats like this are needed to remind the staff of how success is achieved.

"Fund-raising isn't just about making money, you know."

"Isn't it?" asked Gavin. I have hopes that one day Gavin might clamber up onto the first rungs of the management ladder, but if he cannot understand simple things like this, I may well be proved wrong.

"No it isn't, Gavin ! We were going to work for that trampoline ourselves. Penny by penny. And in the process we were going to bring people into the Centre, we were going to be drawn closer together, ourselves, we were going to work as a team. He's spoilt it all."

To take another example I think I know something about, to some people a Leisure Centre could be judged a success or a failure by the number of people who use its facilities. But the mere statistics of attendance are no reflection of the importance of the Centre to the community. As another wise man once said, there are lies, damned lies and statistics.

When Brian Kitson, the Southern Areas Inspector, called to assess the way Whitbury New Town Leisure Centre was serving the people of the region, I will admit that even I was concerned that he might not show the imagination required to smell the success of our little corner of his Area. I even expressed my doubts to Julie, who is always such a pillar of support in times of crisis.

"Totalling up the attendances for each day does rather emphasise the occasional nought, doesn't it? Couldn't we show them weekly, or even monthly?"

"You could show them annually, Mr. Brittas, and you'd still barely make it to double figures."

That is of course not strictly true. There was the old man in the swimming pool whose towel was really disgusting. That's one. There was that little boy I barred for not using the footbath, and the other one who I had to evict when he stuck his chewing gum to the underside of a bench. That's three. There were the six people so unfortunately killed in the machine gun incident, and the four old ladies from the Sunshine Retirement Home who were injured in the same series of events, so that brings us into double figures already. If we add the several hundred members of the Classical War Society who besieged the Leisure Centre (without, I will admit, officially buying their tickets for admission to the Centre), then the statistics start to look rather healthy.

As I said to Julie, "Numbers aren't everything in this game. We need to look behind the numbers to see the real heart and soul of the place." It is not *how many* people come to swim, to play badminton or to take part in aerobics classes. It is the *quality* of those who attend. In acknowledging the true success of our efforts at the Leisure Centre, I could paraphrase Sir Winston Churchill by commenting that never in the field of human physical development has so much been offered by so dedicated a staff to so few.

Good old Bri Kitson saw it that way too. That's why he's an Inspector.

"Numbers?" he queried Julie's concern.

"Well, nobody ever comes here."

"Well, Julie," he said in his kindly, avuncular way, "You'll probably learn as you grow older, as I myself have learnt, that numbers aren't everything in this game. I remember in the days when I ran my own centre that we didn't always have huge attendance figures - but we had something else, something far more important. We had a dream, Julie. A dream..."

I could not have put it better myself.

Southern Areas Inspector Brian Kitson understands the Dream.

HUMOUR

I know when to laugh, and when to let my hair down. Laughter is a true release in this age of anxiety and uncertainty (see RELAXATION below). But there is no time for laughter right now. Do we laugh when we dream? We do not. And I have a Dream.

You should not think, however, that my sense of humour... hold on a moment.
Yes, what is it, Laura?
Oh.
Laura tells me that some people do indeed laugh when they dream, notably her estranged husband Michael T Farrell III. The mind boggles. But then Laura herself sometimes laughs when there is nothing funny happening, although in all other respects she is a tower of strength.

LAUGHTER – THE CORRECT TECHNIQUES
Laughter is a potentially powerful weapon in any Senior Manager's armoury but must be used sparingly and with great precision. Follow my guidelines and you won't go far wrong.

Politely deferential.
This formal laugh should be used when meeting superiors, visiting dignitaries, or members of the Royal Family.

Warm and Welcoming.
Suitable for use when greeting colleagues of similar seniority or minor Royals such as Prince Edward, but only if he has said something particuarly witty.

But where was I? Oh yes.

You should not think, however, that my sense of humour is not as well developed as the next man's. Except possibly Michael T. Farrell III's. I have made plenty of very amusing jokes in my time, although not everybody gets the point of them every time. I remember once remarking to Colin, in a light-hearted and entirely unserious way that as he was being even less efficient than usual that morning, if he had time he could take a length of rope up to the roof, attach one end to the lightning conductor, the other to his trouser zip, and jump off. But only if he had the time.

Now most people would have noticed the bantering style in which the remark was delivered, and would have realised that I was only joshing with him. When a few minutes later we were looking at the security videotapes to check whether a Mr. Jackson, a maths teacher as I remember, (and another name to add to the list of people who attend the Centre. I knew it was wrong to suggest that we never quite make it into double figures) was telling us the truth when he claimed that 20p got lost in the coffee machine, what did we see but a bulky and poorly

Full Blown.
A good guffaw is an effective way to salvage a difficult situation and always helps to put staff at ease when they have done something stupid.

Sincere.
Good for explaining simple rules to less astute members of the public.

dressed man with a bandaged hand carrying a length of rope.

"It looks like Colin," I said to Tim, who was sharing the videotape checking duties with me.

"So it is. Why is he carrying all that rope?"

"Oh no. He wouldn't."

"Wouldn't what?"

"Colin... I told him earlier to, that is, I told him to get some rope and jump off the roof."

"And that was a joke, was it?" Honestly, I can understand a person like Colin not getting it, but you would have thought a quick witted person like Tim would be able to see a joke when it reared up in front of him.

"Of course it was a joke. Not even Colin could take that seriously. Could he?"

He hadn't. He wasn't up on the roof at all. He was in the swimming pool electrocuting fifteen Pentecostalists.

The Chuckle.
Works well with small children and old people.

Relaxed.
Loosen up. Let your hair down. Enjoy.

INDEX

INTRODUCTION

Welcome to Sharing The Dream. This book is my manifesto for the 21st century, a work as important in its own way as Lord Archer's Kane and Abel or Rosemary Conley's Hip And Thigh Diet. It encapsulates my own personal Philosophy Of Life, my way of coping with life's little accidents and disappointments, such as the loss of a job, being shut up in a chicken coop in Bulgaria for two weeks or the complete demolition of one's place of work due to a misunderstanding with an oil tanker. This seminal work, containing the distilled wisdom of all the works of science, business and literature which have shaped my

unique understanding of how to make one's way through life, will teach you all the arts of management, of organisation, of communication, of healthy living, of concentration and of relaxation. I know my Shakespeare, and I'd rather be than not to be; I have read Milton, I have even used his sterilizing mixture for the twins; I have studied Freud, both Clement and Emma; and I have suffered with the protagonists through every subtle twist of the plot of Five Go To Kirrin Island. Drawing from these literary masterpieces, as well as from events in my own life, my book Shares The Dream.

The importance of this book is such that it cannot, of course, be made available to just anybody who turns up at a bookshop with the correct money. Certain criteria need to be fulfilled before the book can be released to them. Do they have three passport-size photographs for identification purposes? Do they have an affidavit from a JP, a Leisure Centre Manager or some other pillar of the local community? Are they wearing jeans? Do they have more than one earring in any ear? Have they ever been fined for the late return of a library book? Only if all questions are answered satisfactorily will the bookshop assistant be instructed to release the book into the hands of the would-be buyer.

So if you are now reading this book at home, rather than furtively in a good bookshop, you have passed the test. Well done. You are one of those chosen to Carry the Torch of World Harmony Through Sport into the next century.

LEADERSHIP

Leadership involves hard decisions. It means not only leading when there are tapes to be breasted and medals to be won, but also being the first there when there are riots to put down and drains to unblock. It is the first rule of Leadership that a leader should never expect those following him to do something that he himself would be unwilling to do. But in this job, there is nothing I wouldn't want to do. If only I had enough time (see TIME MANAGEMENT AND TIMETABLES below) and enough pairs of hands and legs (see PHYSICAL FITNESS below), then I would do everything myself. A good leader knows how to delegate.

Colin, however, is not yet quite a leader. As an illustration of this fact, I can point to the time when there was a slight health hazard in the swimming pool after a dog had forgotten himself at around the eight foot mark.

"You're in charge of the pool, Colin", I said, conducting my own little management test to see whether Colin had learned anything at all since he became a valued member of the team.

"Leave it to me, Mr. Brittas," he replied. He turned towards the lifeguard's seat. "Linda! Little job for you." Actually it was a big job (ha! ha! See HUMOUR above), but I let that pass.

"One of the things you will learn about leadership, Colin, is that if there's a dirty job to be done, you don't get someone else to do it. You do it yourself."

"You mean.... you want to do it, Mr. Brittas?"

My response was a withering stare.

"I'll go and get my trunks and a polythene bag", said Colin, learning fast.

How the results of Colin's efforts came to be delivered to my office in a box, I will never know.

LEARNING FROM MISTAKES

One of the great truths of life, which I have learned from close observation of human frailties over many years as a Leisure Centre Manager, is that people do not change. The leopard does not change its spots. Nor does Colin, for that matter. He just oozes pus from different pores.

The tragedy is that all of you, however carefully you take to heart the words I am writing here, are doomed to repeat your mistakes over and over again. It is not in human nature to learn from mistakes, because you do not recognise mistakes in yourselves. If you could earnestly examine the motives behind your behaviour and find out why others of us find it so unacceptable, then there may be hope. But that requires you to be aware of your own unacceptable behaviour, which in turn requires somebody like me to point out the bits we don't like. And I don't have time to talk to you all individually in turn to assess your social deficiencies. I just hope you will recognise yourselves in some of the people I do have to deal with, and take remedial action from there.

A leopard not changing its spots.

But I doubt it.

One mistake that proved a valuable learning experience for me occurred when Southern Areas Inspector, Brian Kitson, was due on an inspection visit and we had a plague of flies in the sports hall. Introducing a pigeon to eat the flies was only partially successful as, having gorged itself on flies, the pigeon then followed its natural inclinations, resulting in more mess. Doctoring some corn with vodka.to incapacitate the bird proved completely useless. It was no longer hungry.

Apparently the Duke of Wellington cleared the Great Exhibition of sparrows in

1851 by employing sparrowhawks. We brought in Mr. Gilbert Wilmot with his eagle, Titan.

Titan ignored the pigeon, but ate all of the vodka-laden corn.

He flew up into the rafters and staggered about, totally inebriated.

Titan's last flight, more of a plummet, really, was short but spectacular.

LOVE AND MARRIAGE

Love and marriage, as I am sure I need not remind you, go together like a horse and carriage. When my brother Horatio was thinking of marrying that Philippa woman, it was not difficult to identify which one was the horse and which the carriage. Still, he came to me for advice.

"Advice! Of course, Horatio," I replied. "Let me tell you the golden rule in these matters."

"Yes?"

"I once heard a wise man say, the way to handle a woman is to love her, simply love her, really love her, love her, love her."

"Yes, yes. I see that. She's a wonderful person," said Horatio, making an elementary mistake. Philippa is not a wonderful person. She is the social equivalent of an uncapped oil well in a guillemot colony. "It's just that marriage is a very big step."

"It certainly is, bruv," I said, with my most encouraging smile. Put people at their ease, however lunatic the plan of action they may be considering.

"You see, it's always struck me that your relationship with Helen is just about as perfect as it could be."

"Well, yes. I am unusually blessed in that respect, Horatio. Yes."

"So how did you decide?"

How does one decide to take the step into matrimony, one small step for a man, perhaps (and for a woman), but a giant leap for mankind, when one considers the normal outcome of marriage, viz. children (see PARENTING IN NINETIES BRITAIN below).

"Well, obviously I was in love with Helen, Horatio, but I also asked myself certain questions. For instance, does she share my interests?" Helen

The happiest day of Helen's life – the day she married yours truly.

does share my passion for the Leisure Industry. "Can she manage money?" Helen can manage money very well, provided I do not give her too much of it at any one time. "Is she honest?" See HONESTY above. And "Are we physically compatible?" Poor Horatio is not allowed to find that out, being a clergyman.

"But the most difficult question, the one that cost me the most soul searching, was 'What sort of mother will she be to my children?'"

I'm not sure that Horatio was prepared to ask himself all those questions, but I find that most relationship problems can be solved if one just focuses on the things that really count - sharing. Will the woman of one's dreams be good at sharing money, and sharing dreams, at sharing a bed, at sharing the joys of parenthood? And if not, how do you get out of the relationship without hurting yourself?

My two pool attendants, Gavin and Tim, represent all that a healthy lifestyle should be, and I must confess that I am amazed that no young lady has snapped either of them up yet. Young Gavin did have a fiancée, but she let him slip through her fingers. Her name was Jennifer Pelham Young, and she came to the Centre once. It was Julie who brought her to my office.

"Have you seen Gavin?", she asked. "Only I've got his fiancée here."

"I'm afraid Gavin's gone to town for me, Julie, to buy a three

Gavin, dressed for pool duty, not general errands.

amp fuse." A good Manager checks that his team are good at the little things and then they may be ready for the bigger tasks.

Jenny was a good looking woman, with slightly staring eyes and a firm handshake.

"Gavin's fiancée! We had no idea, did we, Julie?"

"Certainly didn't."

Jenny turned out to have been away for five years, after the tragic death of her parents, who were scientists, specialising in the study of oceanic mammals. She and Gavin had been engaged for five years, seven months and fourteen days. All the same, when Gavin reappeared from his shopping errand, he did not look overjoyed.

"Oh Gavin! It's wonderful to see you," cried Jenny, throwing herself into Gavin's arms. Being married to Helen, I can confidently say that I recognise a passionate kiss when I see one, and what Jenny gave Gavin was a passionate kiss.

> ## FORTHCOMING MARRIAGES
> ### Mr. G. Featherly and
> ### Miss J. Pelham Young
>
> The engagement is announced between Jennifer, only daughter of the late and much lamented Professor and Mrs. Archibald, who perished in an aeroplane crash in the Bering Straits two years ago, and Mr. Gavin Featherly, once of Derby and now of Whitbury. The wedding will take place as soon as Miss Pelham Young is ready to take her place in society again.

"Now, you two lovebirds are going to want to spend some time together – in the rest room, I suggest, Gavin." There is a place for everything. As the wise man said, there's a place for us, somewhere a place for us, peace and quiet and something or other wait for us somewhere.

As Tim and I strolled down the corridor towards the gym to set up the volleyball court, I could not help but show my surprise.

"Who'd have thought it, eh, Tim? Did you know they were engaged?"

"No. No I didn't."

"Well, he certainly has landed on his feet, hasn't he! Beautiful, intelligent and apparently rather wealthy - the ideal partner, I'd say." Those difficult questions about money, shared interests and physical compatibility seemed already to have been answered.

Tim was not as enthusiastic in his view of the situation. "Yes, perfect. Absolutely perfect."

"Tim, do I detect a note of bitterness there?"

Tim said nothing. He just threw away the two halves of the pencil that he had snapped in his fingers.

"But how could he do it to me, Mr. Brittas?" It is gratifying to know that all members of my staff turn to me in times of trouble. Like a bridge over troubled water.

"Tim," I said, trying to ease his mind, "I think the best thing is for you to think about how Gavin must be feeling. Think how happy and excited he must be at the prospect of spending the rest of his life with someone beautiful and gorgeous and warm-hearted and who obviously adores him. Now you wouldn't want him to miss out on that, would you? Is that any help, Tim?"

Tim began crying. Were they happy tears of joy for his friend, or sad tears for his own selfishness? It's good to know that my few words helped.

"There's something rather impressive about it, isn't there, Tim? A young, full blooded male, whose fiancée goes away for five years, and he doesn't so much as look at another woman. There's temptation everywhere, we all know that, and from some very attractive ladies, even if none of them work at the Leisure Centre. As the saying goes, you can dance every dance with the guy who gives you the eye, let him hold you tight. But don't forget who's taking you home and in whose arms you're gonna be, darling, save the last dance for me."

ESCAPED HEIRESS RECAPTURED

Whitbury, September 9. Wealthy orphan arsonist Jennifer Pelham Young, who disappeared from the Baumberger Institution for the criminally Deranged while on a day release to visit an aunt, was recaptured this afternoon at Whitbury New Town Leisure Centre, where she had gone to visit her fiancée, gymnasium attendant Mr. Gavin Featherly. During the course of her visit, she attempted to set fire to the Leisure Centre Manager, Mr, Gordon Brittas. After her recapture, Dr. Baumberger commended Mr. Brittas. "We've been trying to get Jenny to release her feelings of rejection by her parents for years, but we have never been able to make her angry enough. Today is a real breakthrough in her treatment. Mr. Brittas clearly has a very special talent."

Things did not go absolutely right for Gavin and Jenny after that, mainly I feel because Jenny spent much of the afternoon tying me up with electric cable and thumping me with a copper pipe. The doctors from the mental home where she had been locked up for five years, seven months and fourteen days seem to think it did her some good, but I am not so sure that it helped me to view her in a favourable light.

"The doctors reckon she's well on the way to recovery," said Gavin, happily. "Mr. Brittas, I don't know how to thank you."

Tim, helpfully identified by the letters T–I–M on his hat.

"It's all right, Gavin. Just think of it as an early wedding present."

"There – er – isn't going to be a wedding, Mr. Brittas."

"That girl's depending on you, Gavin! You can't cast her aside just because she's mentally unstable."

"No, it's not that..."

"Some very successful marriages are to mentally disturbed ladies. At least you have the advantage of knowing beforehand, and not finding out two days into the honeymoon." As can happen. They tell me.

MANAGEMENT

There is more to management than merely keeping your desk clean and your filing up to date (though not much more - that's most of it): there is also the importance of creating clear corporate structures and lines of responsibility (see FLIP CHARTS AND NOTICE BOARDS AND THEIR USE IN LEISURE CENTRES above), although inevitably these lines seem to start and end with me. There is the importance of Sharing The Dream with all those who have a stake in your business operation. And there is attention to detail. With these attributes, you will be a successful manager.

I have over the years attended many courses on Management and been given many copies of books on the subject, with titles like "Introduction To Management" and "Frontiers of Management". I've got a pile of books which has "Thriving On Chaos" on the top, "Creative Management" somewhere in the middle and "The Effective Executive" at the bottom, under "Assertiveness At Work". I've never read any of them, because I have an instinctive grasp of the skills of creating and developing an organization and these books would not be able to teach something which cannot be taught.

Managing a place like Whitbury New Town Leisure Centre is the finest job in the world, but let nobody tell you it is easy. I was once asked to give a talk to a group of my peers in the leisure profession about my management philosophy. I had to stress to them that management is a tough game to play. It's all very well keeping the files up to date, delineating the approved customer parking areas clearly and ensuring that there is a stock room full of pink, blue, yellow and green A4 paper and seven different shades of highlighter pens, but that is not where a good Manager's responsibilities end.

A good Manager sees the problems which may arise before they actually do so. A good Manager spots those small things that have to be dealt with at once before they grow into something more serious. I have never been one for 'crisis management', as some of these business gurus call it, because I believe that nothing should ever be allowed to turn into a crisis. I think my record at Whitbury speaks for itself in this regard. And at Aldershot before it was razed to the ground. As I have told Colin time and again, "We do not have catastrophes in this Leisure Centre. We have problems which we share and cope with."

MUSIC

The difference between a sporting activity and a leisure activity is that a leisure activity can be done to music. Thus badminton is a sport while synchronised swimming (every Thursday at 4 pm in the pool) is a leisure activity. Chess is a sport but square dancing (Friday evenings with Tim and Gavin) is a leisure activity. I run a Leisure Centre, so music is a very important part of my life.

I have a signet ring, which has printed on it one line from an immortal song. 'Climb ev'ry mountain, ford every stream' it says (actually the engraver got it wrong so it reads 'Climb ev'ry mountain, fork every stream', but the point is still well made). That sums up much of my philosophy of life at work. There is another song, a recent dance number which shows that I can 'get down and boogie' with the best of them, that sums up for me in its majestic lyrics the scope of my Dream. It goes, 'There's no limit, no no limit, there's no limit, no no limit, there's no limit, no no limit, there's no limit, no no limit, there's no limit, no no limit.' How true those words are, and how important it is that the impressionable young can understand, in the inspirational words of a popular song of the day, that there is indeed no limit, there's no limit, no no limit.

At home, I think my perfect marriage is encapsulated in the words of the wonderful song which appears on side two of The Best Of Neil Sedaka Today, 'Love Will Keep Us Together'. Helen plays that tape in the car all the time. It also contains the songs 'Little Devil', 'King Of Clowns', 'One Night Stand', 'Solitaire' and 'Our Last Song Together'. Helen says it sums up all her hopes and dreams.

PARENTING IN NINETIES BRITAIN

Sharing The Dream is more than just telling your inferiors at work what to do. It is more than telling the whole world what to do through the medium of a book such as this. If you really believe in the Dream, then it must last more than one generation. We must look for people who will Carry The Torch into that great future, into a time when we will be no more than defaced photographs on a Leisure Centre notice board (see FLIP CHARTS AND THEIR USE IN LEISURE CENTRES above). We must become parents.

In this I am more blessed than most. Thanks to the wonders of heredity, I, a twin, am the father of twins by my dear wife Helen, who also owns three children from an earlier rather unfortunate marriage. (Poor Helen has not always been lucky with her husbands). So I have plenty of experience in playing the role of parent, experience that has helped me ensure that the Dream will last from generation unto generation.

Britain these days is a completely different place to bring up a child compared with Britain of thirty years ago, when my parents were doing their job on Horatio and me. The past is another conurbation, as somebody so wisely said, and to that I would add that the past is a conurbation without sufficient leisure facilities. I remember it well. Our parents tried their best, and I think they succeeded. We've certainly come a long way from Jellicoe Mansions, Romford.

My dad, Jim Brittas, is the salt of the earth. A simple man who is easily embarrassed into feeling out of place when mixing with his socially superior sons, but the salt of the earth nonetheless.

I think Dad sees his life as a bit of a failure. He's raised a family, of course, and he's been a good husband to dear old Mum, but all in all, I can see his point. When

I was forced to bring my birth certificate to work when Julie questioned the existence of my father.

CERTIFICATE OF BIRTH

Birth in the parish of _____ ROMFORD

No.	When and where born.	Name, if any.	Sex.	Name, and surname of father.	Name, surname, and maiden surname of mother.	Occupation of father.	Signature, description, and residence of informant.	When registered.	Signature of registrar	Name entered after registration
114	Romford Maternity Hospital	Gordon Wellesley Brittas	Boy	James Brittas	Jane Brittas formerly Finch	Night Watchman	[signature] Jellicoe Mansions, Romford.	25 April 1958	[signature]	

Birth Certificate issued by **R. I. CALLOW**

Registrar for the Parish of **ROMFORD**

[signature R. Callow]

P

he was a teenager, as he used to tell us almost incessantly, all he wanted to do was to be an astronomer. When he was fifteen years old, he asked his Mum and Dad (my Gran and Grandad) if he could stay on at school and try and pass an exam or something. But Grandad just laughed. "If you want to look at the stars," he said, "we can fix that." And that's how Dad started as a night watchman.

Of course, the older generation's theories of parenting still hold water, but the environment of today's world has changed so much that the young parents of today need a new set of guidelines to live by. The Doctor Spock generation are being replaced by the Beam Me Up Scottie generation. Today, Leisure Centres can assume a pivotal role in the raising of children in the way that the council swimming baths never could when I was a lad. And it's not just a question of banning kids for misuse of chewing gum or for leaving their bikes in the disabled parking spaces. It's more a question of preparing them for the great outside world,

The cynical attitude of children to parents and the young to the old was clearly illustrated when I disguised myself as 72-year-old Mr. Didcot and visited the Leisure Centre incognito. My cover was soon blown as Helen decided on that day to produce the twins. The best laid plans...

for the Game of Life (see GAME OF LIFE above).

My introduction of the twins, Matthew and Mark (good Christian names, none of these strange Darrens or Damiens or Gavins), into the Whitbury New Town Leisure Centre was the occasion of their christening, performed by Horatio on what turned out to be not our best day. The whole thing was meant to be a celebration of new life being accepted into the great family of sport, so of course we went to some trouble to make sure that it was all planned and rehearsed down to the last detail. The christening run-through did, admittedly, lack Helen and the twins, not to mention Horatio and Uncle Herbert, but with eager stand-ins from among my staff (I had to close the Centre to the public for just a few hours while we planned all this).

In the end, the christening went well. Or at least, it happened. Everyone who was meant to be there was there, including the twins and Helen. The fact that the service was conducted by Horatio in the toilets, half drowned out by the sound of the urinals, and that the party afterwards had no guests and that I spent three hours on my hands and knees up to my armpits in a soil pipe, for reasons that I need not go into here, barely diminished the joy that Helen and I felt at the introduction of our twins into the world, a world of Leisure in which they one day will be standard bearers.

There is more to parenting than just getting the Christening to run smoothly. Carole brings up her children in a set of drawers in reception, which I do not approve of, and despite a broad-minded attitude to the social difficulties faced by the unwed parents of today, I certainly do not consider that the right way to be a mother. Even the best appointed chest of drawers cannot ever really take the place of a father. How can a drawer give guidance through life's little maelstroms? How can a filing cabinet dandle little men on its shoulders? Can a cupboard, with or without hanging space, teach a lad to play cricket? Will a drawer, even with two firm polished wooden handles, be able to read a good night story to a sleepy little chap? I think not.

Single Parents are, needless to say, cared for properly at Whitbury New Town Leisure Centre. We have our S.S.S. - the Single Swimmer Special (also known as Special Offer no. 847) - which clearly states that 'any single parent accompanied by a child on a weekday morning may use the facilities between 9.40 and 3.35, at one third of the standard winter season price - or completely free if they've moved into the area within the past three months.' All the Single Parent needs is the rent book to prove that they have recently moved into our community, and there you are. It couldn't be simpler.

Carole cleaning the children's drawers. Office furniture doth not a Father make.

PHYSICAL FITNESS

Physical Fitness is what a Leisure Centre is for. It is the foundation of the Dream - World Peace And Universal Love Through Physical Well-Being. Physical fitness is the reason for the existence of every Centre, and is so important that it cannot be offered to just anybody who walks in off the street.

I have a chart on the wall in my office which shows that only 20 to 30 year olds play squash, but that does not matter. Old people do not need exercise, apart from the occasional game of croquet or cribbage, and children get enough by running around and getting in the way all the time. So that just leaves a few adults, who are the ones we want to persuade to play squash or badminton or take part in our SlimTrim classes. They have to understand the dress codes first, of course (booklet DC/21 gives the full details, but the most obvious rules are no black soled gym shoes, no tattoos on the knuckles of the left or right hands bearing the message LOVE, and no heavy metal rock band T-shirts).They also have to satisfy the other rules of the Leisure Centre, like being able to exercise alone.

I like to think that all those who appreciate what Whitbury New Town Leisure Centre has to offer in the way of physical fitness training do indeed make use of our facilities.

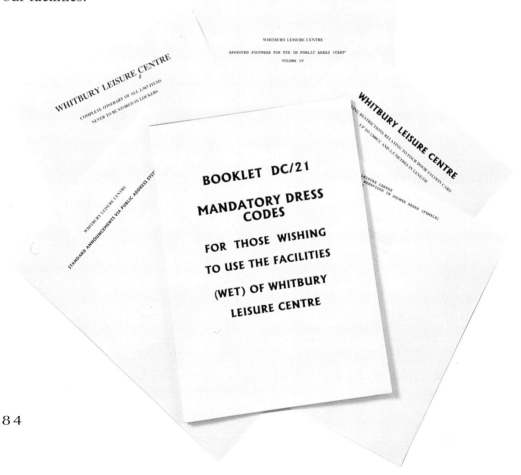

PUBLIC SPEAKING

P

Public speaking is a difficult skill, but one which must be mastered by anybody who wants to be a successful leisure industry executive. Fortunately, I am not afflicted by nerves or a stammer, or embarrassing bodily gestures such as scratching one's private parts or picking one's ears as Colin does, nor do I have an irritating voice which might grate in the way that Tim's possibly over-educated tones might do. There is no easy set of rules to follow, although I have learnt for myself that if pictures paint a thousand words, then why can't I paint you?

Let me take you back to a seminar that we ran at Whitbury a year or two ago. It was called 'Expansion In The Leisure Market'. I wrote a rather moving opening speech, which thanks to the unfortunate electrification of some Pentecostalists during a baptism ceremony in the swimming pool, never quite got delivered. However, I have the opportunity now to remind myself, and you, of the important points which I raised for debate during that conference.

When speaking in public, holding your hands in front conveys warmth and sincerity in a quasi-religious manner.

"Ladies and gentlemen, fellow managers," I would have said if only Colin had not tossed that two bar electric fire into the pool, "I bid you welcome to Whitbury Leisure Centre." A straightforward opening gambit, sincere but without any unnecessary humour at this stage. We remind ourselves who we are: 'Ladies and gentlemen and fellow managers'– and where we are: 'Welcome to Whitbury Leisure Centre'. So far, we haven't put a foot wrong.

"It is my proud duty this morning to introduce our opening speaker, the Member of Parliament for Truro, the honourable Sebastian Coe." Now we have to tell the audience why I am speaking to them, and also to whet their appetite for what will come next (Sebby). Of course, this may create difficulties if the speaker who will follow is not as gifted a public speaker as I am myself, but this is a risk one has to take. Anyway, the audience did not come to hear Seb speak, they came to look at him and see if he was really as small in real life as he appeared on the television in the 1988 Olympics.

"But before Sebby, I'd like to take the opportunity to share with you a few thoughts on what I think this conference is really about." At this point one can almost feel the audience's enthusiasm for the subject, as they settle back to hear a well-reasoned discussion around the themes of the seminar. It does not matter if you overshadow the speakers who come after you: that is their problem, not yours or your audience's, however unfair it may be to someone like Sebby to have to follow a speaker of my experience and with my – what's the word? – fluency with the English language.

Hands behind creates a definite air of confidence and authority.

"The official title of the conference may well be 'Expansion In The Leisure Market', but do we not here have the opportunity to paint on a rather broader canvas? I think we do." This sort of rhetorical question, which the speaker answers himself, is a perfectly natural and acceptable device for the skilled orator to employ. Sometimes questions like this will excite responses from your audience. I remember once being asked to make a speech to an audience of several hundred of my leisure industry peers. The audience had dwindled to only a few true professionals as I moved into the second hour of my discussion on the use of footbaths to control entry into swimming pools, and it was about then that I asked the question, "Do we concern ourselves enough about the spread of athlete's foot in the community? Do we know the meaning of suffering?" A voice from the floor shouted, "Yes!", which was of course the right answer, but the rhetorical question is not there to be answered from the floor.

"I was sharply reminded of the weighty responsibility we all hold the other day" - straight into a true story which allows the audience to relate to the world of the speaker, and to take heart from learning from his experiences - "when a young woman on my staff came to me for some advice." I suppose that describing Laura as 'young' is stretching the truth a little, but a little artistic licence is allowed in great speechmaking. "She was up for promotion, off on her first big interview, and you could see the pleading in her eyes. 'Help me, Mr. Brittas,' (note the reintroduction of one's own name into the speech, just to remind everyone who they are listening to). 'Tell me what this managing a Leisure Centre is all about.'" Incidentally, it is not strictly necessary to do the funny voices when quoting other people. I know that Laura is a woman, but I saw no need to do a funny high-pitched squeak just to get the point across. Though if I'd been quoting Carole, I might have done, I suppose.

"And I told her exactly what I'm going to tell you now." At this point the audience can sit back and relax, because they know they are in for a really good story that may take twenty minutes or half an hour, and they will quickly lose interest in wondering what Seb Coe sounds like or even looks like. They just sit there, mesmerized by the sound of my voice.

"The most important thing to remember is that you are not applying for the post of Leisure Centre Manager." This gives them a jolt: 'But isn't that what it would have said on

If your hands are fastened neither in front nor behind you will find them flapping manically around almost anywhere and you will look like a presenter on children's television.

the application form?'. Get your audience thinking. It stops them daydreaming. Then hit them with the punchline. "That's not the half of it. You are seeking responsibility for the moral and physical welfare of every person in the community. You'll have to be a lot more than manager. You'll have to be social worker, you'll have to be critic, you'll have to be friend, you'll have to be father". Or in Laura's case, mother. Perhaps that is why she didn't get the job. I've never fully understood what let her down.

Expand on the theme. Don't stop while you are in full flow. Give them the benefit of the wisdom that comes from experience. "Where else but in a Leisure Centre can we draw together the troubled strands of our society?" (Another rhetorical question. A shout of 'In Wormwood Scrubs' from the scruffy looking fellow third from the right in the back row should not be tolerated). "Where else will you find young and old, of every class and race, playing with each other on the gymnasium floor? And where can ordinary people find meaning and purpose to their lives, a sense of commitment and caring, a feeling of hope in their grey and insignificant existence?"

Move into the triumphant crescendo of the speech, the moment in which people realise that what you have to say is not interesting, not stimulating, not merely exciting, but something quite different altogether. "Is it, I wonder, an exaggeration to say that we, the Leisure Centre Managers, hold the future of civilisation in our hands? I think not. You may say I'm a dreamer, but I'm not the only one. I hope some day you will join me, and the world will be as one." I am particularly proud of that finish: words that sum up my attitude to the Leisure Industry, and express the way that we can give it the Expansion that the seminar organisers were looking for.

After all that, even the Honourable Sebastian Coe would be an anticlimax.

HANDY HINTS FOR PUBLIC SPEAKING

CUT OUT AND KEEP CARD

Things you will need when delivering a speech

 Glass of water to lubricate your mouth

 Packet of mints for fresh breath

 Alarm clock to help limit yourself to 2-3 hours

 Stout shoes. You will be on your feet for some time

 Light snack. Undernourished speakers can faint from exhaustion

 Dentures. If you wear them, the speech and probably the snack will be impossible without them

RELAXATION

R

The health of the mind is not, if my brother Horatio will forgive me for saying it, entirely a matter of religious enlightenment. We will never succeed in our aims of peace, harmony and a winning national football team unless we all learn the art of relaxation. To be relaxed is essential if we are ever to do things properly, and the secret of relaxation is confidence. If you are confident that what you are doing is right, that what you are doing is being done to the best of your ability, and that no criticism can deflect you from your chosen course, then you will be truly relaxed. I am relaxed.

Colin seems to be able to relax by dressing up as a cowboy and stomping around to Country and Western music. I'm sure it brings on his eczema.

Unfortunately, not everyone around me has the knack of relaxation. When I was shortlisted for the position of British Representative on the European Leisure Industry Standards Committee, a vital role in the shaping of the leisure industry as it surges into the 21st century, I needed my dear Helen to be fully relaxed when we were having dinner with the selection committee. With decisions to be made by the Committee every day on the thickness of gym mats and the height of cubicle doors and the like, it was an extraordinarily important post but one I knew I was made for, one in which I could spread my Dream across an entire continent. All it needed was for Helen to be at her best that evening.

I said to her, "Helen, this is possibly the most important day of my life. It is absolutely vital that you be witty, charming and, above all, relaxed." But it did not work.

We even tried hypnosis. The hypnotist, rather a shady character called Silverman, explained that it could help people overcome trauma, tension, psychosomatic disorders and worry, so we thought it might be worth having a go on Helen. Silverman had already relaxed the rest of my team so much that Colin said, "I love you" and took off his trousers whenever anybody said the word 'need', while Carole punctuated every sentence with a croak like a bullfrog at night, and Linda could only speak in barks and growls. I'm not sure that his treatment of them did much for the relaxation levels in the Centre, but once he

turned his attention to Helen, things improved. She really did relax, and although I decided nevertheless not to take the risk of asking her to accompany me on that vital dinner engagement. I took Laura instead.

A bullfrog. Carole sounded like one of these.

RULES (THE)

R

The trouble with sharing anything is that not everybody understands the rules of share and share alike. This is even more important with something like a Dream, where there may not always be enough to go round. Dreams do not come free, you know.

Thus there must be rules to everything, including the sharing of dreams. In order to live an ordered life, to play the game correctly and to eat your slice of the dream pizza without taking any of your neighbours mushrooms or pepperoni by mistake, we must all understand the Rules. I have taken the precaution of publishing the Rules for the Centre in a simple two volume work, one volume covering the rules for the Centre and all its Dry facilities, and the second dealing with the rules for the Swimming Pool, with a special chapter on foot hygiene.

There is nothing unusual or complicated about them.

Who could quibble with the requirements for enrolment into the Junior Dolphin Club, for example? I quote Volume Two of the Rule Book, page 142, paragraph 3.4.18:

'Children under the age of sixteen are not allowed into the pool unless accompanied by an adult (for the definition of 'adult', see Volume One, page 28, paragraph 7.1.6 (b): 'Definition of Adults'), or unless carrying a membership card to prove enrolment as a member of the Junior Dolphin Club. Membership of the Junior Dolphin Club is free, and all that is required is the filling out of a simple form (form 284/C: Junior Dolphin Membership). This form asks for details of name and address; date of birth; parents' name and address (if known); parents' National Insurance numbers; school name, address and class; name and address and date of birth of class teacher; two recent photographs; some means of identification such as a library card or a savings book; an estimate of swimming standard on a scale of 1 to 10 (from shrimp through halibut and jellyfish to salmon and killer whale); and an

Gavin caught in blatant breach of the directive in Volumne Four of the Rule Book (staff) Page 212 paragraph 17.4.3 (a) and "consuming comestibles outwith a designated nutrition break". Naughty.

officially approved swimming costume in black, dark blue, green, red or white. Please also refer to the notice board: THE DANGERS OF SHARING SWIMMING COSTUMES.'

Whenever prospective new members come to the Centre, we ask them to bring with them two references from GPs, solicitors, bank managers, priests or registered property owners, as well as a doctor's certificate (providing that the doctor signing the certificate is not also one of the bearer's referees). Then the probationary membership period of six months has to be satisfactorily served, with at least three attendances at the Centre each month and participation in no fewer than four nor more than eight Centre tournaments or competitions (see Volume One, page 312, paragraph 2.0.8., subsection 5, 'Tournaments and Competitions'). And then you are in! What could be easier or fairer than that?

It is not only in the way we enable the general public to participate in the Centre which requires clear guidelines. My staff, too, need always to know where we all stand in relation to each other and the way we run the Leisure activities together. The welfare of my staff has to be my first priority. Sometimes my staff inadvertently act in breach of the Rules, as for example when Colin led his

Colin copied out the Whitbury New Town Leisure Centre Safety Manual (all 560 pages) ten times onto 300 old envelopes, 780 ticket stubs, 85 pharmacist's bags, 3 bread wrappers and a used Elastoplast.

Whitbury New Town Leisure Centre

Rules Governing The Parking Of Motor Vehicles

Section 1/1A (cars up to 1300cc, two door)

Cars in this category may be parked in bays 14–26 Mon–Fri (except Bank Holidays) and must be left with their headlights facing outwards

Regulations dictate that a member of staff should always be on hand at the pool with a life-saving device, but if Colin were to leap in we would probably be in contravention of EC rules regarding the quality of the water in the pool. Quite a dilemma.

daughter to believe that he and not I was the Manager. Impersonating a Leisure Centre Manager is a serious offence. You could probably get shot in the Army for something like that. That is why we have closed circuit television security cameras, that is why we have a Staff Discipline Book and that is why I am always conscious of the need to protect them from themselves. I do not know how often I have told Colin that chain saws and power cables do not mix, for example, but despite his copying out the Safety Manual ten times, he does not always understand. That is why we do not allow unmarried female members of staff to work in the Centre at night unless chaperoned by a married female colleague. And that is why Council By-laws and both volumes of the Safety Instructions for Minors are required reading for all new members of my team.

Then there are the rules that cover a wider spectrum than just the Leisure Centre (although you will probably agree with me by now that there is nothing that really covers a wider spectrum than the Leisure Centre, because that encompasses the Dream). I am referring to the laws of the land, manufacturer's instruction manuals and coded Council instructions in the event of insurrection. I should not be telling you this, as it is probably a state secret, but at any outbreak of civil disturbance, The Whitbury New Town Leisure Centre has been designated a rallying point for those still loyal to the Crown.

The laws of the land are worth knowing. The Employment Act of 1985 and the Criminal Enforcement Act of 1984 are the two that I come into contact with most frequently during the normal course of events at the Centre, so I tend to know the major clauses of those two off by heart. It was, however, under the terms of Section 4 of the Misuse of Drugs Act 1971 and the Offences Against The Person Act of 1861 that I was charged (and found entirely innocent) after that

TIME MANAGEMENT AND TIMETABLES

Time Management is such an important subject that I have reserved an entire section (shared with a dissertation on timetables, of course) for it. If we do not use time properly, if we cannot condense our thoughts into a few pithy words, if we cannot convey the essence of ideas without repeating ourselves or without repeating ourselves, nor without unnecessary obfuscation, how can we Share The Dream? At the Whitbury Leisure Centre, we organise three day Time Management Courses, which I confess barely scratch the granite surface of this complicated yet crucial life skill. The longer course has been tested on some of the workforce, but their Time Management skills are so underdeveloped that I could not spare them for the three months needed to complete the entire programme. Except Colin, I suppose. I wouldn't mind him going off somewhere other than the Leisure Centre for three months.

I have a simple solution to Time Management problems. I pace my day in segments of two minutes at a time. My staff are now familiar with my reassuring call of "Back in two minutes", which lets them know that I will very soon be able to turn my attention to the next problem on the day's agenda. During my sponsored silence, I even went as far as to print up a notice that read BACK IN TWO MINUTES, and I used it all the time. It is a very unusual problem which requires more than two minutes to reach a resolution, or at least to get unmanageably out of hand, by which time we are probably better employed looking at the next problem anyway.

DATE	DAY	TIME	SCHEDULE
3rd	Monday	8.58 – 9.00	Arrive. Park car in Manager's slot.
		9.00 – 9.02	Enter reception. Greet Carole.
		9.02 – 9.04	Proceed upstairs to office. Greet Julie.
		9.04 – 9.06	Enquire into whereabouts of Julie. Avoid Colin.
		9.06 – 9.08	Prepare papers for 9.10 staff meeting.
		9.08 – 9.10	Check Helen has taken children to school.
		9.10 – 9.12	Staff meeting. Proceed to staff room.
		9.12 – 9.14	Take staff roll call.
		9.14 – 9.16	Enquire into whereabouts of Julie.
		9.16 – 9.18	Explain plan of action for morning.
		9.18 – 9.20	Remind staff of lunchtime staff meeting.
		9.20 – 9.22	Proceed on tour of inspection.
		9.22 – 9.24	Inspect gymnasium area. Pass it.
		9.24 – 9.26	Inspect pool area. Fail it.
		9.26 – 9.28	Inspect reception area. Pass it.
		9.28 – 9.30	Inspect pool area. Fail it again.

Our life at the Centre is built around my Timetable. Nobody is allowed to make changes to the timetable, as it is delicately balanced and poised to give a structured duty roster of responsibilities for all members of the Team. Even during August, traditionally a quiet time for us, the timetable keeps us all in the right place at the right time. The result is that we now have a sensitively run well oiled administrative machine, honed over the years to cope with any crisis, from Colin's late arrival due to a weeping boil on his left buttock to Gavin's knocking off early to take advantage of

the discounts on duvets at Debenham's. Without the timetable, the Centre would be a vastly different place, with people moving in an unstructured way around the complex building, without purpose and without ambition. How can you enjoy your leisure time unless you discipline yourself? How can people live without a framework in which to exercise? If time is money, then there is no such thing as 'free' time. A Leisure Centre is there to develop us as human beings, to make the world a better place, and not just to help us enjoy ourselves in idleness. The sooner everybody realises that, the better it will be for all of us. Especially for Leisure Centre Managers.

Dividing my working day into two minute segments involves getting up at 5 a.m. to fill in the 240 boxes on my 8-hour time management sheet before going to work.

WORLD PEACE

W

Without world peace, how can the Dream be fulfilled? We cannot set up a world government without world peace, we certainly can't bring people together and promote team spirit, and I don't see how we can hope for the end of war unless we get world peace first. Or at the same time.

World peace is more than just everybody stopping fighting each other. It is more than persuading customers at the Leisure Centre not to open fire with machine guns when their 20p coin gets stuck in the coffee machine. World Peace starts with the little things, like my scheme to award a Friendliness Prize (a pair of best plastic sunglasses) to any child who comes to the Centre and speaks to at least four other children they'd never met before. It grows to bigger things, like freedom from hunger, which I have achieved within the Leisure Centre by instituting a system of regular checks on the crisps and chocolate vending machines (form VM/22), and by making sure there are always a regular supply of biscuits for Helen in the canteen. It develops through global moves like Horatio going off to to be Dean of Beirut, giving him the politically and spiritually exciting challenge of banging a few heads together in the cause of peace. One day, it is our Dream that there will be members of the Brittas family in every troubled part of the world, changing things by their very presence. A Brittas in Bosnia, a Brittas in Belfast, more Brittases in Cambodia, the Middle East, the Falklands, the Vatican and several in Letchworth. That's a violent town if my last visit is anything to go by. Fights breaking out all around me, in the bus station, outside Woolworth's and in the garden of the Peter Pan Old Folk's Home for no reason at all.

One day, we all hope to be able to say those wonderful words, "Happy Christmas, War Is Over". We are certainly getting there. No outbreak of full-scale war has been reported in Whitbury since I moved here.

Could this be the key to World Peace?